PATRICK HENRY,
FIREBRAND OF
THE REVOLUTION

FIREBRAND OF

ILLUSTRATED BY VICTOR MAYS

PATRICK HENRY
THE REVOLUTION

By Nardi Reeder Campion

j'B
H 396ca

LITTLE, BROWN AND COMPANY   BOSTON·TORONTO

*Published simultaneously in Canada
by Little, Brown & Company (Canada) Limited*

PRINTED IN THE UNITED STATES OF AMERICA

To

Narcissa Martin Reeder Whitehouse,
Colonial Dame of Virginia.
In love of country and zeal for action she is
a match for Patrick Henry.

"People are ruled by words."

Disraeli

"The people I want to hear about
are the people who take risks."

Robert Frost

"The secret of freedom is courage."

Pericles

Acknowledgments

I want to thank these people who have
helped me in the preparation of this book:

Thomas Campion, and Tom, Tad, Toby, Cissa, and Rus-
sell Campion — editors extraordinary
Colonel Red Reeder — author, editor, and military his-
torian
Dorothea Darrah Reeder — editor
Mrs. Pinkie Sanford Perry — invaluable assistant
Rosamond Wilfley Stanton — typist and consultant
Robert Marshall, Jr. — student editor
John Goodbody — Vice-President of Colonial Williams-
burg
Richard M. Ketchum — American Revolution authority,
Associate Editor, *American Heritage*
Stewart Johnson — Research Editor, *The New Yorker*
Colonel Empie Potts — military historian
Helmuth Joel — Bronxville School History Department

Cynthia Sykes — typist
Mrs. Elizabeth Martin — Head Librarian, Bronxville Public Library
The ladies of *Nondescript* — a unique literary society

Patrick Henry, Firebrand of the Revolution would never have been written had it not been for Tad Campion, who suggested this project after seeing the remarkable Williamsburg movie, *The Making of a Patriot,* written by Emmet Lavery, directed by George Seaton, and produced by William H. Wright of Paramount Pictures. I am indebted to colonial Williamsburg for permission to quote from this movie.

A special citation must also go to Toby Campion for his tireless after-hours work on this book, to Cissa Campion, the complete baby-sitter, and to Thomas Baird Campion, senior, hero of the home front.

Contents

PATRICK HENRY,

FIREBRAND OF
THE REVOLUTION

chapter 1

The Boy Who Hated School

THE schoolmaster stood before the children in the shabby one-room school and announced proudly, "Our new slates have just arrived from England. Give me all your string. I'll thread it through the holes in the slates and hang them around your necks."

The slight, sunburned boy in the front row quickly tried to stuff a fishing line into the pocket of his homespun breeches. Too late.

"Pah-trick," said the teacher, "hand me that fishline."

Slowly the boy delivered up his line. In horror he watched the teacher cut it into short lengths. Going, going, gone. Patrick Henry would pull no catfish out of the Paumunkey River this autumn afternoon. Pat closed his blue eyes in despair.

"Now," said the schoolmaster, after distributing the new slates neatly hung on Patrick's line, "copy and solve this problem:

$$9373783648454563901423894$$
$$\times 9567489203796021596127 6$$

Pat moaned and rested his forehead in the palms of his hands.

"Pah-trick, why are you not working?"

"No use."

"*No use?*"

"When will I ever need to do a problem that looks like this?"

"Master Henry, you are stupid and you are rude. Rise to your feet and deliver the Lord's Prayer, spelling each word correctly before you pronounce it."

"Oh, sir, I can't."

"Can't indeed!" shouted the teacher, grabbing a peach-tree switch. "Never say *can't* to me, boy." He whipped the lad sharply across the legs.

Patrick scuffed through the dry leaves on his way home. Slowly his spirits began to rise. It had been a bad day in school, but every day in school was a bad day for him. He and school mixed about as well as Indians and fire-water. But once out in the woods, Pat began to be himself. He stopped to inspect his "slope," a fish trap he had built across Totopotomy Creek. The brisk stream was named for one of Pat's heroes, Totopotomi, chief of the friendly Paumunkey Indians. The slope was filled with enough fish to feed the whole Henry family. Patrick forgot all about school.

He wished he could live outdoors all the time. He had heard tales about boys captured by the Paumunkeys who, when they were released, refused to go home. Pat understood how they felt. No school, no teachers, just camping out, fishing and hunting. My, didn't it sound fine! He wished a nice friendly Indian would kidnap him.

The liquid notes of a cardinal's whistle floated through the pines. Pat pursed his lips and repeated the call. Uncle Langloo had told him to try to learn the language of the birds and he was working at it. Patrick wanted in every way to be like his mother's brother.

Langloo Winston was a mighty hunter who spent most of his time living with the Indians. He fished with them, talked with them, even dressed like them. The Indians adored Langloo, until he fell in love with the chief's daughter. That made them fighting mad. For a week they besieged him in a log fort. Langloo and three Negro slaves defended themselves with guns, until the chief's daughter went out and stopped the fighting. Patrick could not understand why Indians and whites should not marry each other if they wanted to.

When Patrick reached home, a young slave named Caesar ran to meet him. Pat gave Caesar a shove and both boys rolled in the red dust, yipping like young foxes. Caesar was supposed to be Pat's body servant, but he was more playmate than slave. Even as a boy, Patrick Henry had no time for class distinctions.

"Watch it, Mistah Pat," warned Caesar, "here comes your Pa!"

"Stand up, Patrick," commanded a stern voice. "Will you never learn manners?"

"No, sir." Patrick grinned.

"Did you do any better in school today?"

"No, sir." Patrick's grin widened.

"March into the house, laddie, and sit down to your lessons. Life is not a joke, my young mon."

Patrick's father could not understand a son who hated school. Colonel John Henry was a serious, scholarly redhead who spoke with a strong Scottish "burr." He and his brother, the Reverend Patrick Henry, for whom young Pat was named, had graduated from the University of Aberdeen in Scotland, and to them education was everything. Colonel Henry, a devout Episcopalian, knew the Bible from cover to cover and read Latin for pleasure. He worked hard and spoke little, and he found it difficult to understand a son who worked little and loved to talk.

When John Henry came over from Scotland, he went to live in Virginia with a cousin named John Syme. Syme died and John Henry married his buxom widow, a spirited girl named Sarah Winston, who became Pat's mother. Colonel Henry's sturdy character was highly respected in Hanover County. Faithful to his God and his king, John Henry's favorite day of the year was when he marched at the head of the militia in the parade to celebrate the king's birthday.

Everyone said Patrick was like his mother. Sarah Winston was charming, musical and gay. She had a gentle nature and a soft way of speaking, but she could be as firm as a rock. The Winstons, who were Welsh, were great talkers with a flare for drama. Unfortunately, they had more talent than they had energy or ambition; but they knew how to enjoy the good things of life.

"Studley," the Henry home, was a two-story brick house surrounded by shady trees, with slave quarters and stables at a distance from the house. There were many acres for a boy to roam over and many children to play with.

Patrick grew up surrounded by girls. He was a hero to his sisters Jane, Sarah, Susannah, Mary, Anne, Elizabeth, and Lucy. His brother William and his half-brother, John Syme, often teased the girls, but kindhearted Pat stood up for them. Some of his gentleness and good nature must have come from his seven sisters. For one important reason, Patrick almost wished he had been born a girl. In colonial Virginia, girls were not allowed to go to school. Few of the women or Negroes could read or write. Pat thought they were lucky.

Patrick was brought up in a cultured Christian home and he received rare benefits from it, including an intimate knowledge of the Bible, with its pure English. From his schooling he gained little. Virginia had a struggle to establish a decent school system. Public education was even considered dangerous. The royal governor, William Berkeley, wrote to England as late as 1670: "I thank God there are in Virginia no free schools nor printing and I hope we shall not have any, for learning hath brought disobedience and heresy into the world."

As troublesome as a stupid governor was the fact that there was little town or village life in Virginia. Houses and plantations were far apart and the only means of transportation were horses or river boats.

Sons of the rich were tutored at home; others went to the miserable country schools. The schools had no blackboards, no maps, no pencils, and precious little paper. For pens the pupils used wild turkey quills, for ink they used a liquid made from roots, berries and a little gunpowder.

The roof of Patrick's school leaked and wind blew through the cracks in the wall. In winter the classroom was cold. Logs for the fireplace were supposed to be supplied by the parents, but there were seldom enough logs. Children of forgetful parents were made to sit in the coldest corner of the drafty schoolhouse.

The country teachers were often men who had failed at other occupations. They were strict, and sometimes cruel. The most important articles in the schoolroom were the switches beside the teacher's desk. Teachers were paid in animal skins, Indian corn, tobacco, peas and beans, and one student sat near the window to hail passers-by and try to increase the teacher's salary by selling the extra vegetables.

By modern standards, colonial schooling was certainly poor; yet early Virginia produced many great men — statesmen, generals, judges, educators and presidents. How were these men educated? The Bible and the Greek and Latin classics seem to be the answer. Colonial children had no light literature of any kind. All their reading was serious.

Almost every day Patrick Henry's father said to him, "Son, why are you not studying your lesson?"

One day Patrick answered, "I can't stand the way they talk in these books, Father. Look at the subtitle of my Latin book: *A Delicious Syrup Newly Clarified for Young Scholars Who Thirst for the Sweet Liquor of Latin Speech.* Why can't people say things in plain English?"

"A good Latin scholar never lacks for the right word, Patrick," his father replied sternly. "One day you will thank me for holding you to your studies."

Patrick often managed to miss school altogether. On the days when he did get there, he spent most of his time thinking up devilment. He was full of mischief and his blue eyes gave off sparks of merriment. Pat was especially clever at getting good boys into trouble. He knew just how to tip over their ink without being seen. After school he liked to invite well-dressed lads to go paddling, and then "accidentally" upset the dugout canoe in midstream. If the boy could not swim, so much the better. Pat swam like a shark and he always managed to tow his howling victim to the sandy shore.

Patrick's parents did not know what to do with him. His father whipped him and prayed over him. Pat nursed his black and blue spots and played his fiddle for comfort. After one beating, Patrick went to find Caesar. "Come on, Caesar, we're leaving."

"Where us goin', Mistah Pat?"

"We're running away. I can't stand being civilized. You fetch the fishing rods and some food. I'll get the shotguns. For the love of heaven, don't let anyone see you."

The boys were gone two weeks, two wonderful barefoot weeks without changing their clothes or washing their faces. They swam in the cool rivers and slept beside campfires under the starlit sky.

One day while they loafed under a weeping willow on a riverbank, watching the motionless corks of their fishlines, Patrick said, "You know what I think, Caesar?"

"What, Mistah Pat?"

"Say, don't call me mister out here in the woods, Caesar. I think there's more 'n one way to get educated."

"Amen, Mist — ah — Brother Pat."

"I'll bet we've learned a lot out here, Caesar, tracking

deer and fox through the forest and living off the land."

"Beats goin' to school, don't it, Pat?"

"Beats anything. I wish we could live in the woods forever. I'd like to be a pathfinder and blaze the way west, walking into a golden sunset every evening, and listening to wild critters howl in the black of night."

"Old Pat, you shore can talk. You got a golden tongue."

Patrick threw himself back on the ground and laughed. Warm sunlight filtered through the leaves and freckled his face. "My Pa says if talk was gold, I'd be rich. But he says *silence* is golden. I like silence all right. Sometimes I go out in the woods to be alone and listen to the silent spinning of my thoughts."

"Lordy, you want I should leave, so's they can spin now?"

"Don't you ever leave me, Caesar. Take off your clothes — I'll race you to the other side of the river. We got to head back home tonight. Father'll whip us purple . . . but it's been worth it."

Colonel Henry punished the boys and Mrs. Henry thought religion might help. She took Patrick to church with her to hear the Reverend Samuel Davies, who was called "The Prince of American Preachers." (Davies later left Hanover County to become the fourth president of Princeton University.) Dressed in a black gown and white wig, Mr. Davies preached a stirring, tearful sermon. He took his text from the sixth chapter of Jeremiah: "They have healed also the hurt of the daughter of my people slightly, saying Peace, peace to our souls; when there is no peace."

"How many of us," thundered Davies, pounding the pulpit, "cry peace, peace to our souls, when there is no peace!"

Patrick, the bedeviled schoolboy who wanted to be left alone to enjoy the peace of nature, thought that was a marvelous quotation.

On the way home Mrs. Henry asked Pat what the preacher had said. She was amazed at the boy's ability to imitate Mr. Davies and repeat the details of his sermon.

Patrick was captivated by Samuel Davies because he was a dangerous figure who dared — out loud — to be different. Everyone in Virginia was supposed to belong to the Established Church of England. But not Mr. Davies. He defied the law by being a Presbyterian. Sarah Winston Henry, who had a mind of her own, joined Davies's flock. Young Pat heard hot arguments between the Henrys and the Winstons on religious freedom.

Patrick was just eleven when his grandfather, bald-headed old Isaac Winston, was tried in court and fined twenty shillings because he let Presbyterians hold services in his home. The trial made an impression on young Pat; he was proud of his grandfather's independence.

Colonel John Henry and the Reverend Patrick Henry, staunch Episcopalians, did not share Pat's enthusiasm.

Colonel Henry conferred with his brother about the problem of Patrick. "This boy of mine is part savage," he complained. "He runs wild in the forest, dividing his time between the uproar of the chase and the silence of the deep woods."

"Perhaps," Uncle Patrick said dryly, "Patrick finds 'sermons in stones and books in running brooks.'"

"Impossible," said John Henry flatly. "I'm at my wits' end and so is the schoolmaster."

"Your boy is not stupid, John. He has acute powers of observation and an astonishing memory. Pat has only to see and hear something once and it is his forever. Have a little patience."

But soon everyone's patience ran out and, at the age of ten, Patrick Henry left school forever. It was a great relief to both Patrick and the school.

Colonel Henry was determined to tutor his son at home. The Reverend Patrick Henry rode over from Slash Church to help him. By hard labor they taught the young "savage" to read and even enjoy Latin, a habit Patrick kept up all his life. The book-hating boy thought the painful Latin drill kept him from the true joys of living, but later it proved invaluable. Patrick's gift for logic and language flowed directly from it.

The Reverend Patrick Henry taught his nephew some math, which the boy almost enjoyed. The minister also gave him a code to live by, most of it from The Book of Common Prayer. Fifty years later Patrick could still repeat it word for word.

> My duty towards my neighbor is to love him as myself:
> To be true and just in all my dealings,
> To bear no malice nor hatred in my heart,
> To keep my hands from picking and stealing,
> To keep my tongue from evil speaking,
> Not to covet other men's goods,
> But to learn and labor truly
> To earn my own living
> And to do my duty in that state of life
> Unto which it shall please God to call me.

By the time Patrick was fourteen, John and Sarah Henry were convinced their lazy, lovable son would never amount to tuppence. He had given no hint, by word or deed, of having the slightest ability to make his way in the world. They need not have worried. The Henrys had eleven children. Ten of them were plain, honest sparrows; but one, for some unfathomable reason, was an eagle.

chapter 2

How Not to Keep Store

A STEADY drone of snoring came from the back pews of Slash Church. Young Patrick Henry squirmed in his seat. He wished he could scratch. Why did you always itch on Sundays? Why was it easy to sit still when you were fishing, and impossible when you were in church?

Uncle Patrick lowered his voice to a chilling whisper: "The Christian life is an active life."

Not in this church, thought Pat.

Uncle Patrick's big voice boomed to a climax: "Our conduct on earth will determine whether or not we enjoy an eternity of happiness in the next world."

Pat moaned inwardly. *So much for fun by-and-by — how about now?*

Suddenly the restless boy sat up straight. Tomorrow was St. Andrew's Day! That *was* fun. His sagging spirits soared. To young Pat, November 30th was the best day of the year.

The Scots who settled Hanover County made a festival of St. Andrew's Day; it was a traditional Scottish celebration. Tomorrow there would be horse races, foot races, wrestling matches, drum-beating and fiddling contests. And to top it all, a great banquet with toasts to the king, the royal governor, and dear old St. Andrew, the patron saint of Scotland.

Patrick knew by heart the notice that had appeared in the *Virginia Gazette*. It proclaimed that:

A pair of Silver Buckles be wrestled for by a Number of Brisk young Men —
A pair of handsome Shoes be danced for —
A good hat be cudgelled for —
A pair of handsome Silk Stockings be given to the handsomest Country Maid that appears in the field —
A pig with his tail soaped be run after and given to the person that catches him and lifts him off the ground by his tail —
A Quire of Ballads be sung for, by a number of Songsters, all of them to have Liquor sufficient to clear their Wind-Pipes.

When St. Andrew's Day dawned, crisp and sunny, poor Pat was lying in bed with a broken collarbone. A wild colt, which he and Caesar were trying to break, had thrown him to the ground.

Pat's mother stayed home from the festivities to take

care of him. Mrs. Henry was handsome and sweet, and surprisingly intelligent. Unlike most colonial ladies, she read books. "Remember, Paddy boy," she said, " 'Sweet are the uses of adversity.' "

"How's that?"

"Shakespeare meant good often comes out of what seems to be bad luck. Perhaps you can turn your broken collarbone into a blessing."

Pat decided it was worth a try. During the long dreary days indoors, he taught himself to play the flute, an achievement that made a broken collarbone seem worth while . . . almost.

When Patrick was fourteen, his family moved to Mount Brilliant, a large estate in the western part of Hanover County. (In those days you did not need much money to buy an estate; land was cheap.) Patrick and his brothers and sisters loved the excitement of moving. The Henrys took all day to make the twenty-mile journey over rough roads, a memorable trip.

Mount Brilliant was built on one of the highest points in the county. Through its rolling acres, the South Anna River rushed to the sea. The surrounding oak and pine woods were filled with wild game. It was a place to delight the heart of a boy like Pat, but Colonel John Henry had no intention of letting this "child of nature" loaf his way through life.

"Son," he said, "what was it Uncle Patrick taught you about work?"

> "To learn and labor truly
> To earn my own living."

"Exactly. The time has come, my boy. I have apprenticed you to Mr. Tate to learn storekeeping. Please try to do yourself credit."

At first, Mr. Tate thought his apprentice was a good clerk. Pat was quick to learn the stock and he never forgot prices. But one day the storekeeper left Patrick alone. When Mr. Tate returned, he stopped in the doorway, thunderstruck. Pat was leaning on the counter talking to two grizzled characters dressed in fur caps and buckskin. A lady in black was trying to catch Pat's attention. She seemed unhappy.

"Whole canoe loads of them French and Indians come a-paddlin' down the Ohio," said one frontiersman. "The French was singin' their crazy songs and the Indians was spyin' out places to put forts."

"Young man," said the lady, "I'm *trying* to buy a bolt of calico."

"Build forts on the Ohio!" cried Pat. "Why that land belongs to us. Virginia goes all the way to the Mississippi."

"Boy! I want a bolt of calico."

Mr. Tate could stand still no longer. He took care of the lady, the trappers, and Patrick, one after the other. That night Mr. Tate called on Pat's father.

"Colonel Henry," he said, "I'm afraid Pat and I must part. The boy can sell goods, all right. The Lord knows he has the gift of gab. But if he really gets gabbing, he don't even *see* the customers. In my business, you only make that mistake once."

John Henry sighed. Patrick was a problem, although not as bad as his older brother William whom Colonel Henry described in a letter as "wild and dissipated." John Henry decided to take his small savings and buy a stock of goods to set his sons up in a store of their own. Perhaps if they were given responsibility, they would settle down.

The Henry brothers opened a store near Hanover Courthouse, on the side of a hill overlooking Courthouse Creek. It had a pleasant, and to Patrick, distracting view. Pat sat for hours in the dim, musty room, inhaling the strong odors of aged cheese and new leather, and looking wistfully out into the bright sunshine. If the day were too beautiful the brothers would depart, leaving behind a sign:

GONE HUNTTIN

Patrick Henry loved guns. He used a single-shot flint-lock which he loaded through the muzzle. This sporting weapon did not slaughter game the way modern guns do. A colonial hunter had to be agile and incredibly accurate.

In those days there were no curbs on hunting. The uncleared forests were alive with foxes, rabbits, squirrels, wild turkeys, deer, wolves, and even bears. For the skilled marksman there was an abundance of quail, duck, pheasants, partridge, and wild geese. The Henry brothers kept their family table supplied with delicious meat.

In the store, day after day, Pat — brother Willie was little help — weighed sugar, drew molasses, and measured off coarse Osnaburg cloth. Patrick's storebook, written with a neat hand and imaginative spelling, is still in existence. Henry Brothers supplied Hanover with everything from "shew buckles" to "sticks-hair" (hairpins). It is evident from Pat's careful accounts that he tried to be a good storekeeper, but the odds were against him.

Sometimes during store hours Pat's bounding health and high spirits simply overcame him. He would leap on Willie, and the next customer who appeared found the proprietors rolling on the floor, thumping each other in great gusts of horseplay. The store looked like a gymnasium.

The country store in colonial times was actually a community center, a kind of club where people met their friends. It took the place of the daily newspaper in conveying village gossip. Before Pat's wooden counters a thousand scenes were acted and a thousand stories told.

To Patrick Henry, whose real interest was people, the country store was a school for the study of human nature. His brother-in-law, Sam Meredith, later declared that Henry's only remarkable characteristic as a youth was his "habit of close and attentive observation." This habit often kept the storekeeper from keeping store.

If the customers were gay and full of talk, Patrick listened with deep attention. If they were dull and silent, he knew just how to set them in motion. He liked to promote arguments, and if the debaters came to blows, why so much the better. Pat's cousin, George Dabney, told Colonel Henry, "Your son has a talent for getting everybody's opinion without letting out what he thinks. He asks questions that seem to have nothing to do with the subject, and then he leads you right back where you began. Sounds like a real lawyer."

"Sounds like a real waste of time," said Colonel John Henry.

Over the plum duff at supper, Patrick entertained his family by imitating the customers. "Now, young man," he said, holding his nose to copy Mrs. Campbell's nasal twang, "that's a scant pound o' sugar. More yet, more yet!" Pat was a born mimic and he could be very funny, but his humor was never mean. Like his mother, he was warmhearted and gentle.

Most of Patrick's customers were men who thought slaves should do the work of the world, which left them free to sit and smoke on the shady porch. Their discussions were endless. The more they talked, the more Pat listened, and the less he sold.

Patrick developed a talent for telling stories, and that also helped slow sales to a trickle. His reputation as a storyteller spread around the county. He liked to spin yarns that aroused his listeners to laughter, or pity, or indignation. Sometimes he scared the wits out of them with ghastly ghost stories.

On stormy days when the store was quiet, Patrick amused himself with his fiddle or his flute. To his own surprise, he also began to enjoy reading. He read a good deal, especially history, but when customers came in, he quickly hid his books under the counter. He did not want anyone to think he was trying to put on airs.

Whenever Uncle Langloo visited the store, he brought excitement with him. One day he came in, brown as an Indian, and announced, "There's gonna be trouble, Pat, my boy. The French mean to have the Ohio and us Virginians ain't gonna allow it."

"What'll you do, Uncle Langloo?"

"*Fight.*"

"Who'll be your leader? The French, with Indian help, will be fierce."

"Young planter from up Westmoreland County. Big fellow and smart. Everybody likes him."

"What's his name, Uncle?"

"I forget. Calls his plantation Mount Vernon."

Pat wished he could go west with Langloo and leave his store forever. Steadily, Henry Brothers store went downhill. Pat simply was not made for business. One day he was stretched out on a bag of salt, listening to a hot debate between two tobacco planters, when a customer came in and said to him, "Excuse me, sir, have you any salt?"

"Sorry," said Patrick without moving, "just sold the last peck." And he went right on listening to the argument.

If commerce was difficult for Pat, bill collecting was impossible. His customers ran up bills and then played on Pat's sympathetic nature as easily as he played on his fiddle. Patrick would believe any hard luck story and frequently, instead of making a collection, he extended more credit to the debtor.

The day came when Colonel Henry had to face the fact that his son Patrick was no better at storekeeping than he had been at school. "Patrick," he said gloomily, "you seem doomed to failure."

Patrick Henry was a hopeless optimist who always saw the bright side of the picture. "Don't worry, Father," he said cheerfully. "I'll come out all right. Adversity toughens a man."

Soon afterward, jobless, penniless, Patrick multiplied his father's worries by falling head over heels in love with a Virginia belle.

chapter 3

The Eighteen-Year-Old Bridegroom

PATRICK drove his father's gig down a dirt road edged with goldenrod. The sky was a deep, cloudless blue and there was a tang in the crisp air. A gust of wind rustled the red splashes of dogwood against the fuzzy-green loblolly pines. It was a beautiful autumn day and love had lit up the world for Patrick Henry.

Pat turned his horse into a part of town called The Forks. He drove through a tunnel of trees and pulled to a stop before Rural Plains, the sturdy brick home of a farmer named Shelton. He bounded up the steps and thumped on the massive maple door. The brass knob turned and before him stood a slender dark-haired girl. She lifted her dark eyes to Patrick's blue ones. Neither one said a word. They just looked.

"Sarah," called her father, "who's there?"

" 'Tis Patrick Henry, Papa."

"Again?"

"Papa!" Sarah Shelton blushed.

She looks like a primrose, thought Patrick. "Are you ready to go?" he asked. He tried to make his voice sound casual.

"More than ready," said Sarah, handing him her crimson cape.

Gleefully, Patrick and his Sarah rode off through the shining October air to the Dabneys' harvest festival. When crops were ripe, it was the custom for Virginians to prepare a big dinner and invite the neighbors to help gather in the harvest. About forty people came to the Dabneys' that day to cut grain and pick corn. The guests worked hard. At the end of three hours, the job was finished and the gaiety and dancing began.

Everybody danced. Girls and boys, old men and old women, capered in jigs and reels. They stepped forward and back and turned their partners round and about. Patrick was a wonderful dancer and Sarah was as light as a bubble. Pat hated to leave Sarah's side to take his turn playing the fiddle.

"Git to your music, boy," said Uncle Langloo. "I'll guard this here girl like she was a hogshead of tobaccy."

"Thank you for the compliment, Mr. Winston," laughed Sarah.

Between dances brother Willie whispered into Patrick's ear, "Come on and have a nip of applejack. A little toddy will do you good."

"No thanks, Will," said Patrick, smiling.

"Blast it, Pat, you can't refuse to take a drink and still be a good fellow."

But Patrick Henry could. He never had anything to do with smoking or drinking, and he was one of the most popular young men in Hanover County.

When it came time for the Virginia Reel — the last dance at every party — Pat took Sarah's hand and looked gravely into her eyes. They did not know anyone else was in the room. When they went outside, after the party was over, the crisp air was filled with music and laughter. The neighborhood slaves had also enjoyed the Dabneys' good food and drink, and now they were sitting around a bonfire, shucking corn and singing as they worked. They took turns doing antic dances and "cutting up." Sarah and Patrick stopped to watch and when Caesar saw them he hopped to his feet and pranced through his version of the Highland fling. He was very funny and the young couple shook with laughter.

Driving slowly home in the chilly moonlight, Patrick and Sarah sat close together. "Sarah," announced Patrick, "I've made an important decision."

"Yes?"

"Yes. You and I are going to get married."

"When?" Sarah's voice sounded small.

"Right away," boomed Patrick.

"But, Pat, my family will never agree. I'm only sixteen."

"Well, I'm eighteen. Together our ages add up to thirty-four. That's enough years for anybody."

Sarah laughed. It was hard to be serious with Patrick.

The Henrys and Sheltons were horrified at the idea of marriage for this rollicking, carefree couple. But Patrick Henry would not take "no" for an answer. He talked and talked, until he wore down the resisting parents. Finally they gave their consent, and even agreed to help support the giddy pair, who had no other visible source of income.

The wedding took place before the open fire in the parlor at Rural Plains. Sarah looked fragile in her white dimity dress. Patrick, who had never been so neat in his life, looked like a firecracker about to explode. Uncle Patrick said, "Repeat after me, 'With this ring, I thee wed.'"

"With this ring, I thee wed." Looking at Sarah, Pat could not keep the twinkle out of his eyes. He was so happy.

After the wedding there was a party. People sang and danced and ate; Patrick and Sarah outdanced them all. Then the happy, penniless pair rode off to Pine Slash, their new home. Their body servants, Dicy and Caesar, went along with them. "Us got to look after these chillun," said Caesar. "They're happy, but they ain't got much sense."

"Speak for youself, boy," snapped Dicy. "Miss Sarah, she got more sense 'n she know what to do wit'."

Sarah Shelton made a good wife for Patrick Henry. She came from a family of farmers, but they valued the things of the mind. Her grandfather was William Parks, the Williamsburg bookseller who published the colony's first newspaper, the *Virginia Gazette*.

As her dowry, Sarah brought Patrick six slaves and the three hundred acres of poor land at Pine Slash. Their new home was crudely furnished, but it was not without books. The household centered around the big fireplace where Sarah and Dicy did the cooking. Above the hand-hewn mantel hung Pat's powder horn and gun. On frosty winter nights the bride and groom huddled round the hearth and dreamed long dreams.

Daniel Boone, who was just a year older than Patrick Henry, said, "All you need to be happy is a good gun, a good horse, and a good wife." To this Patrick added, "And a good daughter." The Henrys' first child, Martha, was born the next year. Pat and Sarah were enchanted with her. They nicknamed her Patsy.

Nobody called Patrick Henry lazy now. He wanted his family to live on the best farm in Hanover and he worked like an ox. He labored right along with the slaves in the fields. Who could have guessed that soon this sweaty, sun-burned farmer would cause the king of England to tremble with rage?

Patrick's bad luck did not leave him when he married. It doubled. He was trying to grow tobacco in a terrible tobacco year. What the worms did not eat, the sun withered. Virginia was forbidden by Britain to coin money, and tobacco was used to pay for everything. No tobacco, no purchases. The young Henrys raised enough food to live on, but they had little else. Except, of course, each other and a happy home.

And then one day they did not even have a home. Three years after their wedding, Pine Slash burned to the ground. This was a cruel blow. Pat and Sarah lost most of their possessions, and they lost their independence. There was nothing to do but move in with Sarah's family.

Mr. Shelton owned the inn across from Hanover Courthouse. This sprawling wooden building (which is still standing) was an important stop-off for travelers going to Richmond or Williamsburg. Patrick helped his father-in-law by tending bar and fiddling for the guests. He did not look very impressive in his coarse clothing, but his wonderful high spirits lit up the tavern. Here Pat got to know many Virginians. He learned to speak the language of the rough and ready pioneers who became his greatest supporters.

One day a burly frontiersman clumped in to see Patrick. "Is it a fact you're related to Langloo Winston?"

"Nephew," said Pat proudly. "Why?"

"You heerd about his great speech?"

"What speech?"

"Oh, it was sumpin. I was there," said the adventurer.

"I was in Langloo's company, fighting the French and Indians. Things was bad, real bad, boy. Day after day it rained. We had no tents, no food, wet gunpowder, and ragtag clothes. Us men was all set to quit. Your Uncle Langloo, he hopped up on a tree stump and made a humdinger of a speech. He let go with fire and brimstone.

When he finished the men yelled, 'Onward! Onward! Lead us to the enemy!' And that's just what your uncle done."

"Zingo!" said Pat. "Words are as good as weapons, aren't they?"

Patrick was impressed. But his grandfather Winston was not. It was just what he expected. Patrick repeated the tale to him, and old Isaac Winston nodded his bald head. "Oh, my boy Langloo can dazzle 'em with words. He's just a natural-born talker like them orating Indians, Tecumseh and Cornstalk. I've heard him speak on election days and he would roll his rich words into the crowd until the very hair would stand on my head and I would cry like a baby."

One day Langloo himself blew into Hanover Tavern to see his nephew and enjoy a flagon of ale. He was dressed all in leather and his skin looked like leather, too.

"How's the fighting, Uncle?" Patrick asked eagerly.

"Capital!" shouted Langloo. "You ought to see our leader. Name's George Washington. Big and tall and fearless, he is, with the strength of a lion and a fierce temper. He keeps that temper chained up, but sometimes in a battle he leaves it go, and then — *watch out*."

Patrick longed to trek off to the frontier with Langloo, but he was a married man and he had to figure some way to support his family. He could not live on the Sheltons forever. The only thing he knew was storekeeping. Perhaps he could learn by past mistakes and make a go of that. He put some of his slaves up for auction to raise money.

The slave auction, with its big block for the exhibition of human beings, made Patrick sick. He was deeply religious and he loathed the buying and selling of people; but it was the way of the time and he had no other means to raise money. He prayed someday slavery would end.

Patrick's second attempt to be a storekeeper was no better than the first, and for the same reasons. His store suffered from the same lack of organization and the same easygoing storekeeper. Pat gave credit to all comers and seldom collected a bill. Before long, P. Henry's store was up for sale. Poverty and debt stared him in the face.

Failure again! Pat took down his gun and went hunting with his friends. He could always find solace in the woods. At night the hunters gathered round the campfire, waiting for the dogs to tree a coon or possum, and listened to Pat tell his sit-on-the-edge-of-your-seat stories. Pat's cares began to melt away.

When Patrick returned from the hunting trip, Sarah met him with good news. They had been invited to one of Colonel and Mrs. Dandridge's famous house parties

over the Christmas holidays. Sarah and Pat both loved a
good party, and to go to the *Dandridges'!* This was exciting, even for Patrick Henry who felt at home with all
kinds of people.

Colonel Dandridge was the wealthiest and most aristocratic gentleman in Hanover County. His wife, Dorothea
Spotswood, was the lovely daughter of the royal governor.
His cousin was Martha Dandridge, "the richest and pret-
tiest widow in Virginia," recently married to Colonel
George Washington in one of the most splendid wed-
dings Virginia had ever seen.

The Dandridge home was the showplace of Hanover.
Silken damask curtains hung at the long windows and
carpets as soft as moss covered the inlaid floors. Crystal
chandeliers filled with glowing candles lighted the rooms,
their gleam reflecting in mirrors and polished table tops.
From the walls family portraits looked out of golden
frames. Slaves dressed in long coats and knee breeches
hurried about, serving spiced wine and cakes to the
guests.

"I didn't know such elegance existed," murmured
Sarah Henry.

"My dear," said Mrs. Dandridge, "I'm delighted you
could come. This is our latest addition, little Dorothea."
The two-year-old girl dropped a wobbly curtsy and Pat-

rick, who loved children, patted her dark curls. Neither the child nor the man dreamed they might one day mean a lot to each other.

"Who's the tall, redheaded lad standing before the fire?" Patrick asked his host. "I don't remember seeing him before."

"That's Tom Jefferson from Albemarle County," said Colonel Dandridge. "Since his father died three years ago, he's been the master of Shadwell. His mother's a Randolph, you know, and they own most of the county. Tom's on his way back to William and Mary. Let me introduce you."

"What are you studying at college?" Pat asked young Jefferson, after they shook hands.

"I hope to read law with Mr. George Wythe," Tom replied. "He's the greatest teacher in Virginia. I mean to be a lawyer, but I want to learn all about science and politics and history, too."

"Why did you decide to be a lawyer?"

"Well," Tom said slowly, "I guess law is one of the most important things in the world. It is said that where law ends, tyranny begins."

"*Where law ends, tyranny begins,*" Patrick repeated. "Interesting. And where does law begin?"

"It begins with years and years of study," Thomas Jef-

ferson said seriously. "But I don't mind that. I'd rather
study than eat."

"There's where we differ," laughed Pat. "Come, let's
begin on that ham right now."

How did it happen that a repeated failure like Patrick
Henry, a roughneck who enjoyed pronouncing his words
like a backwoodsman ("Natteral pairts," he told his horrified father, "are better 'n all the book lairnin' on yearth")
was invited to spend the holidays in the home of a famous gentleman like Colonel Dandridge? Perhaps the answer can be found in this word-picture, drawn by the famous pen of Jefferson. Recalling his first meeting with
Patrick Henry, the third President of the United States
wrote:

> My acquaintance with Mr. Henry commenced in the
> winter of 1759. On my way to the college I passed the
> Christmas holydays at Col. Dandridge's in Hanover, to
> whom Mr. Henry was a near neighbor. During the festiv-
> ity of the season I met Mr. Henry in society every day
> and we became well acquainted altho' I was much his
> junior, being then but in my seventeenth year, and he a
> married man.

> His manners had something of coarseness; his passion
> was fiddling, dancing and pleasantry. He excelled in the
> last and it attached everyone to him. Mr. Henry had a

little before broken up his store, or rather it had broken him up; but his misfortunes were not to be traced either in his countenance or his conduct.

Patrick "excelled" at pleasantry, and "it attached everyone to him." Small wonder he was invited to the Dandridges'. Patrick Henry was the life of the party.

Driving home in the open carriage through light, blowing snow, Patrick said to his pretty little wife, "Tom Jefferson told me he's going to be a lawyer. I think I'd like to learn something about the law."

Sarah moved closer to Pat, tugging the bearskin rug around her. "You could be a lawyer if you wanted to, Pat. You can do anything when you put your mind to it."

Patrick accepted this dubious statement with a grin. To most people, Patrick was a cheerful failure. To his wife, he was a man with unlimited possibilities. We all tend to live up to the picture others have of us, and lucky is the man who has someone to believe in him, even when facts point the other way.

chapter 4

The Loafer Turns into a Lawyer

A SECOND and third child were soon added to the Henry household. Patsy and her brother John now had little Edward to play with. Patrick Henry had five mouths to feed, and no job. Even to an optimist like Pat, things began to look critical. It was necessary, it was urgent, that something be done. Patrick mounted his horse Shandy and cantered through the woods to consult his long-suffering father.

"Patrick," sighed Colonel Henry, "I don't know what to suggest. You've failed at every turn."

"Well, I don't seem to be cut out for trade," said Pat.

"That's an understatement," said his father. "What are you cut out for? You only studied what interested you. You couldn't grow tobacco and you can't run a store. You're twenty-four years old. You have a wife and three children and no money. The future looks bleak."

Patrick nodded his head. His only pride was that he had no pride. "You're absolutely right, Father," he agreed. "I can't sell anything and I can't raise anything, but — well, I can talk."

"Talk!" cried his father. "You call that a help? With you, Patrick, talk is the curse of the devil."

Patrick threw back his head and laughed. "Maybe, but it's my only wisp of talent and I mean to use it. There is just one business in Virginia where I can put my 'cursed' tongue to work, and that's in the practice of law."

Colonel John Henry's jaw dropped. He could only repeat what he thought he had heard. "*The law?*"

"Yes, sir. I've spent hours listening to the debates in Hanover Courthouse and I've decided that's what I want to do. I'm going to be a lawyer."

"Son," said his father, "you've always had the most optimistic view of what you can accomplish, but this time you've outdone even yourself. What makes you think you have enough sense to be a lawyer?"

Patrick was silent. How could he answer such a question? "Well, Father, I think brain power develops from exertion — not relaxation."

"I cannot believe my ears," said Colonel Henry. "Is this you, Patrick Henry, telling me what I have repeated over and over?"

Actually, Patrick Henry had qualifications for the law that made up for his sketchy education. He was blessed with an excellent memory, a quick wit, and a talent for knowing what was important. He was a steady reader of the Bible, which left its imprint on his thought and speech. In any fight, he was for the underdog.

Pat understood people, old and young, rich and poor, educated and ignorant. He liked them and they liked him. He knew he could stir men and bring them to his way of thinking. He had done it by the hour.

Physically, Pat could take on his weight in wildcats. His tall body was as strong and agile as watch-spring steel. He had no nerves and a well-controlled temper. He was light of foot and quick of tongue, and he possessed powers of leadership that he had not even discovered.

Patrick studied hard. He read *Coke on Littleton* and *The Virginia Laws* until he knew them by heart. "Listen to this," he called to Sarah. "Coke says no Englishman can be taxed unless he has a chance to vote for the tax himself, or else someone who represents him does it. The Magna Charta guarantees it. What do you think of that?"

"So —" murmured Sarah, who was busy with her sewing. Her mentality was no match for Patrick's lively mind. Like most Southern ladies, she agreed with her husband and flattered him, but made little attempt to keep up with his opinions. In old Virginia, the world of ideas was strictly for men. Years later when Thomas Jefferson visited Paris, he was shocked by the way Frenchwomen talked politics. He wrote home that he hoped the good American women would continue to "soothe and calm the minds of their husbands and leave political debate alone."

Patrick allowed himself six weeks of uninterrupted study. At the end of that time he kissed Sarah and the children good-by and set out for Williamsburg, determined to get a license to practice law.

"I hope I'll pass that examination," Patrick muttered. "Tom Jefferson said it takes years of study to become a lawyer."

"You can do anything, Pat," said Sarah, and she meant it.

It took Pat and Shandy four days to travel the seventy miles between Hanover and Williamsburg. The spring rains had begun and the road was a hopeless sea of mud, dotted with islands of stumps. Patrick Henry had never been to Williamsburg before. The beautiful capital of Virginia dazzled the young countryman. Even the cold April rain did not dampen his spirits. As Shandy sloshed through the puddles on Duke of Gloucester Street, Patrick gaped. What an exciting town! There were handsome brick houses surrounded by box hedges and shops with many-paned windows curving outward. Colorful signs swung in the wind. Sounds of music and laughter floated from the tavern doors and smoke curled from brick chimneys. The air smelled to Patrick as though everyone in Williamsburg were having ham for dinner.

At the end of Duke of Gloucester Street Patrick pulled up before a large brick building. This was the College of William and Mary where he would find his friend Tom Jefferson. Tom, Pat discovered, had literally lost himself in books. There were books on his desk, books on the shelves, even on the floor.

"By heaven, it's Patrick Henry of Hanover!" exclaimed Tom. "I'm glad to see your cheery face on this dreary day. What brings you to Williamsburg?"

"I've come to be admitted to the bar — I hope." Patrick's mouth grinned, but his blue eyes were steady. He was in deadly earnest about getting a license. This was his last chance; everything depended on it.

"You're going to be a lawyer?" Tom tried unsuccessfully to hide his astonishment.

"I don't wonder you're amazed, Tom. I even surprise myself when I say Patrick Henry, attorney-at-law, but that's the title I'm seeking."

"Could you be ready to apply for a license so soon?" Tom looked at the stacks of books around him, books it would take him years to master. Jefferson was seven years younger than Patrick Henry but he sounded years older.

"Tom, law is a bottomless pit. Nobody's ever really ready to become a lawyer. I've studied some, but I've decided the best way to learn law is to practice it."

"More power to you, Pat! Such courage calls for a cele-

bration. Come with me to the Raleigh and we'll have a feast."

The white Raleigh Tavern with its many dark shutters

was not like the rustic taverns of Hanover County. Patrick was impressed. "I didn't know an inn could be so handsome," he said.

"Oh, there are thirty other taverns or ordinaries right around here, but people of quality prefer the Raleigh." Young Jefferson did not mean to sound snobbish. He pointed toward the tall trees that bordered the wide brick sidewalk. "We call those wineglass elms because of the long slender trunks and the curving branches at the top. Handsome, aren't they?"

Pat nodded. His sharp eyes were fastened on the leaden bust of Sir Walter Raleigh above the front door of the inn. "I wonder if Sir Walter did us more harm than good by making tobacco king in Virginia."

"Why?"

"Using tobacco for money is chancy. Take my Uncle Patrick. He's a minister, you know, and his salary is sixteen thousand pounds of tobacco a year, no matter what tobacco is worth."

"Yes," laughed Tom, "with the clergy it's feast one year and famine the next. And speaking of famine — but before we dine, let me show you the Apollo Room. It's my favorite."

Patrick looked in wonder at the elegant high-ceilinged ballroom with the graceful blue paneling and dark polished floor. He read aloud the motto gilded over the mar-

ble mantel, HILARITAS SAPIENTIAE ET BONAE VITAE PROLES
— "Jollity is the offspring of wisdom and good living."

"Your Latin's in good shape," said Jefferson. "That's important for a lawyer. Isn't this a great room? I bring my 'Fair Belinda' here to dance. She does a fetching minuet."

"Belinda?"

"Rebecca Burwell of Carter's Grove. She's the belle of Williamsburg. I mean to marry her one day, if she'll have me."

Over roast pork and cold cider, Tom warned Patrick about the Examination Board he had to face. He leaned across the pine table, his reddish hair glowing in the candlelight. "It's a frightening group, Pat, some of the outstanding lawyers in America. There's Robert Carter Nicholas. He's highly respected, a pillar of Virginia. Very conservative. Then there are the two Randolphs. John is Treasurer of the colony and his brother Peyton is King's Attorney. They grew up at Tazewell Hall, the family estate here in Williamsburg, and both of them went to William and Mary. Their father, Sir John Randolph, is the only man born in Virginia ever knighted by the king. All the Randolphs have generous natures. The brothers may take pity on you."

"Let us hope so." Patrick rested his chin on the palms of his hands.

"But George Wythe!" Young Jefferson rolled his eyes.

"I plan to study law with him myself after college. I'd hate to face Mr. Wythe in an examination without knowing everything. He was the first professor of law in America. With him law is not a profession, it's a religion."

Patrick moaned. "The devil of it is each one of these giants quizzes me *separately.*" He shrugged his heavy shoulders and grinned. "Well, if I fail, it won't be the first time. One thing about hitting bottom, there's no place to go but up."

"Here's luck to you," said Jefferson, lifting his goblet of cider. "You're going to need it."

Thomas Jefferson's picture of the Board of Examination proved accurate. George Wythe refused to have anything to do with the uneducated upstart from Hanover. Robert Carter Nicholas refused at first, but after Patrick's repeated promises to do further study, he finally agreed. The amiable Peyton Randolph signed Patrick's license and told Jefferson years later, "Young Henry was ignorant of the law, but I could see he was a man of genius and I did not doubt he would soon qualify himself."

It was the courtly and elegant John Randolph who caused all the trouble.

A polished wit and a profound lawyer, Mr. John Randolph was shocked by Patrick Henry's rustic manners and ungainly appearance. He refused to question the bumpkin. "The law," he said rudely, "is a profession for gentlemen."

"But, sir," said Patrick, "I've already gotten two signatures. Surely a man of your fairness and wisdom would not dismiss me without a hearing."

Reluctantly, John Randolph threw out a few questions. Patrick Henry's answers were sharp and to the point. Randolph sat up and listened. This was no bumpkin. He asked a more difficult question. The answer came back straight and true.

John Randolph differed, or pretended to differ, with everything Henry said, and almost before they knew it the two men were deep in controversy. Randolph used all his highly developed debating skills. He drew Patrick out with questions and baffled him with unexpected arguments. He would lead the young man down one line of reasoning, then suddenly switch to another. Patrick surprised his wily opponent with bold and even original answers. Their discussion lasted several hours. It developed into a kind of chess game, each man cleverly plotting to trap the other.

At last John Randolph threw up his hands. "Young man, you defend yourself with brilliant logic. Let's see what the lawbooks say about this." He pulled a leather volume from the shelf. "Incredible! Here are lawbooks you have never seen, yet you are right and I am wrong. My boy, you have taught me a lesson. You must forgive me for saying it, but I will never trust to appearances again." Randolph drew a silk handkerchief from his sleeve and wiped his brow.

"Mr. Henry," he continued in rolling tones, "if your industry be half equal to your genius, I know you will become an ornament and an honor to your profession." John Randolph took a quill pen from his desk and signed the license with a flourish. Patrick Henry had won his first case.

It may seem odd that a loafer could turn into a licensed lawyer so quickly, but in colonial times poor legal training was not unusual. There was not a single law school in America. Even great lawyers like George Wythe and John Marshall were poorly prepared for their bar examinations. Brilliant legal scholars like the Randolphs, Thomas Jefferson, and John Adams were the exception, not the rule, in the colonies.

A jubilant Patrick Henry turned his horse toward Hanover that April afternoon. He could not wait to tell Sarah the news. She was no longer a Mrs. Nobody. She was now the wife of an attorney-at-law.

After twenty-four years of drifting, Patrick Henry was on the right road at last.

chapter 5

Patrick Sets Hanover Afire

"THE king is dead! Long live the king!"

The historic words rang through Virginia in the autumn of 1760. News of George II's death stunned the colony.

The coronation of the new king, George III, was celebrated in high style in the colonies. Colonel John Henry, who loved royal occasions, donned his scarlet uniform and tricornered hat. With a rattle of drums and a fanfare of trumpets, he assembled the militia on Hanover Courthouse green. The colonel barked a brisk command and the red-coated soldiers formed a regimental box; then they fired a musket salute to the new monarch. As the band played "God Save the King," Colonel Henry's patriotic blood pounded. He marched his men smartly around the village green. The crowd cheered and set off fireworks.

As soon as the celebration ended, the colonel crossed the road and entered Hanover Tavern to look for Patrick. The boy was not turning out to be the slipshod lawyer one might have expected. A reputation for getting things done was being added to Pat's popularity. No one could have been more surprised than his father.

Colonel Henry did not find his son celebrating with the merrymakers in the taproom. Instead he was upstairs reading before a crackling fire.

"Is this a new Patrick Henry?" demanded the father. "Where were you at the celebration?"

"Father!" Patrick jumped to his feet. He was always glad to see the stern, Scottish father whom he so admired. "Celebration? What is there to celebrate? We all know George the Third is a stubborn numbskull. What good will he do Virginia?"

"Patrick!" Colonel Henry was shocked. "I do not understand such talk. In my day, no young man would dare raise his voice against our king."

"That's just it, Father. He's your king, not mine. You were born in Britain and you idolize the Crown. To me, King George is just a young man, two years older than I am, whose first act as king was to dismiss America's friend William Pitt — the best prime minister we ever had. What a stupid thing to do! George the Third is not my kind of man."

"Well, keep it to yourself," snapped Colonel Henry. "In Scotland we disagreed with the English, but no Henry was ever disloyal. You are not to ridicule the king of England, Patrick."

Patrick opened his mouth to say something, and then closed it. He knew when to change the subject. He lifted a paper from his desk. "Look at this, Father. Cousin John Winston has given me a case. He wants me to sue Mr. Spencer for calling him a hog-stealer." Patrick read from the paper, letting his big voice thunder out the words: "After said Spencer did utter, publish, and declare aloud that I, John Winston, was a hog-stealer, much scandal, many and great crimes were then blamed upon me."

Colonel Henry could not help laughing. "Your mother's family ought to keep you in business."

"Business, yes. Cash, no. I am suing this same 'hog-stealer' right now because he owes me three pounds. As for dear old Uncle Langloo, if I could collect for all the legal work he thinks up, we'd be rich. The Winstons love to sue, but hate to pay."

"There's an old German proverb," Colonel Henry remarked with a chuckle, "that says 'Doctors clean the body, preachers clean the soul, and lawyers clean the purse.' A good Scot, I might add, keeps his purse snapped shut. I'm glad you're making some money at last, Patrick, lad. Hold onto it."

During his first year as a lawyer Patrick Henry, ex-loafer and perfect failure, served sixty clients. His fee books show that most of his clients, unlike the customers at his store, paid their bills. People began to realize happy-go-lucky Patrick had become a hard-working and capable attorney. By the end of three years, Patrick was supporting his wife and five children, two new daughters, Anne and Elizabeth, having recently arrived. He soon began to give financial aid to both his father and his father-in-law, much to their amazement.

When Patrick was twenty-seven he took a "hopeless" case which changed the whole course of his life. Most people thought Pat was on the wrong side, as indeed he was. Nobody thought he had a chance to win; but everyone wanted to hear his arguments, because he was arguing against the ministers of the Church of England, a daring thing to do.

The ministers claimed their salaries had not been properly paid. It was Virginia's strange "tobacco-money" that caused the trouble. Trade with England brought in British goods, not British money, and so the planters began to use tobacco for money. They put the tobacco in large warehouses and in return got certificates which became the main currency of Virginia.

The law required every parish to pay its minister a salary of sixteen thousand pounds of tobacco per year, no matter what tobacco was worth. When the price of tobacco was high, the clergy were paid handsomely. When prices dropped, they almost starved.

Drought ruined the tobacco crop one year and many

planters were almost wiped out. Because tobacco was scarce, it doubled in price, but the clergy demanded their sixteen thousand pounds of tobacco anyway. They seemed not to care what hardships this brought on their people. A bargain was a bargain, they argued. When tobacco was cheap, they had said nothing.

The people complained bitterly. In every tavern men discussed the parsons' sudden wealth at the expense of their poor parishioners. Uncle Langloo was one of the most indignant. "Seems to me, if them parsons had wanted to help out, they'd have prayed for rain. All durin' that blasted drought, did any one hear 'O, Lord, let it rain'? Oh no, indeed. I think maybe they *wanted* a drought. The Indians got a rain dance works better than what these parsons put out."

"Cool down, Uncle Langloo," Patrick said. "Cool down. The Burgesses have passed a law fixing ministers' salaries at twopence-per-pound of tobacco, regardless of what the market does. That ought to take care of everything."

"Not very likely," said Langloo. "The old buzzards in black will prob'ly pray their way out of that. They may not be fittin' to bring rain, but give 'em a salary cut and they'll rare back and move mountains."

Langloo was more prophetic than Patrick. The parsons were enraged. There was only one person who could help them — the king of England. They sent violent appeals to

George III. He was quick to sympathize with the clergy.
"I declare the law passed by the House of Burgesses to
be null and void," boomed King George.

As soon as the parsons heard the good news, they went
to court. They wanted to collect all their back salaries,
beginning when tobacco went sky high. No one dared
take the case against the clergy — no one except Patrick
Henry. His father was one of the judges in the court, and
his uncle was one of the protesting ministers, but that
did not stop Patrick. All his life Patrick Henry did exactly
as he saw fit, no matter what other people said.

The Reverend Patrick Henry could not believe his
ears. His nephew — his namesake — was going to appear
in court against the clergy? Impossible! The minister
jumped on his horse and rode to Hanover Tavern.

"Patrick!" he cried. "What's this gossip I hear? Surely
you would never stand up and argue in court against
the clergy of the Church of England! I do not believe it's
possible."

Patrick looked down at his feet. For a moment he did
not answer. Then he raised his blue eyes and looked directly into his uncle's dark ones. "Uncle Patrick," he said.
"I am as sympathetic with the clergy as you are; especially so, on account of you. I know our ministers deserve
every possible consideration. But, Uncle Patrick, this case
is much bigger than ministers' salaries. This is a case

where the king of England has interfered with the rights of the people. He has brushed aside a Virginia law passed by the House of Burgesses. We cannot allow the British king to stifle the voice of Virginia." Patrick said the last sentence slowly, his deep voice booming forth.

Uncle Patrick seemed lost in thought. He stroked his chin and nodded his head absently. "Patrick," he said, "I don't agree with you; yet I am strangely moved by your words. The common law of England gives the king absolute authority over his peoples, yet perhaps — I say perhaps — men may have a God-given right to rule themselves. It's an odd thing, Patrick, but I believe every great speech in history has been made by someone who was advocating the law of God over and above the law of man. That's just what you say you are doing."

"Ah, Uncle Patrick, then you do understand my point of view?"

"Perhaps. But I thoroughly disapprove, make no mistake about that."

"Will you do me one favor? Will you please stay away from the trial?"

"Why?"

"I will have to say some harsh things about the clergy, and I don't want to hurt you. Besides, if I saw you there it might strike me with such awe that I could not do justice to my clients."

"In that case, perhaps I should come and help the clergy," laughed the Reverend Henry. "But since the clergy is well established and you are a young lad just getting started, Patrick, I'll heed your request and stay away. Bless you, my boy."

Uncle Patrick rode back to Slash Church. He was not alarmed by the case. He was sorry to see his nephew take up a hopeless cause, but at least the boy was familiar with failure.

Crowds of people pushed through the brick arches of Hanover Courthouse to hear the trial. Farmers in homespun breeches and muddy boots jostled plantation owners dressed in velvet and powdered wigs. The twenty parsons in black and white robes looked like penguins. On the slaves' bench Caesar sat rigid as a ramrod, his eyes glued on his master. He and Langloo and Sarah were the only ones in the room who believed Patrick had a chance.

All the cards were stacked against Patrick Henry in the Parson's Case. The clergy engaged the best legal talent in the colony. Patrick's opponent was the Irish-born Peter Lyons, an older lawyer with a great reputation. His poise made Patrick seem youthful and awkward. Colonel John Henry, sitting on the judge's bench, blushed at the contrast between his country-bred son and the learned royal counsel.

"Oyez! Oyez!" the court crier intoned — and the trial began.

First the jury had to be chosen. The jurors were selected from the crowd outside the courthouse. The defendant, Reverend James Maury who represented the parsons, objected. Reverend Maury, one of Thomas Jefferson's teachers, was used to dealing with aristocrats. "These men are from the vulgar herd," he said. "I have never heard of any of them. They are not gentlemen."

Such snobbery was firewater to a young democrat like Patrick Henry. "Sir," he cried, "these are honest Virginians and therefore beyond reproach!" The crowd cheered. Patrick had scored his first point.

The jury remained as chosen. Some of the jurors were Dissenters — people who wished to break away from the Church of England — and therefore they were naturally sympathetic to Patrick's side.

Peter Lyons spoke first. He composed a flowery tribute to the clergy and concluded by quoting the king of England's decision. "It only remains," said Lyons, "for the jury to fix the amount of back wages that should be paid to the Reverend Maury and the other clergymen, and we shall waste no more valuable time on this matter." He sat down and patted his brow with a lace handkerchief.

Hesitantly, Patrick Henry rose to his feet. Everyone knew him, but no one had ever heard him make a real

speech. He did not himself know if he could do it. He
shuffled his feet and cleared his throat. He said a few
stumbling words. The audience stirred with embarrassment. Colonel Henry slumped in his seat. The parsons
exchanged sly looks, as if victory were at their fingertips.

And then, Patrick straightened his shoulders and began to talk. In sharp, clear sentences, he explained that all
wealth comes from the men who labor in the fields. He
pictured the farmers toiling under the blazing sun and
fighting the rains of spring and the frosts of autumn.
Then he pictured the clergy, living on the fruits of other
men's labors, dressed in silken clothes and riding in car-
riages.

As his words began to flow, Patrick's eyes seemed to
pierce the minds of his listeners. The people were caught
in his spell. One man said afterward, "There was a pecul-
iar charm, a magic in his voice."

Patrick's arguments mounted, and a "deathlike silence"
fell on the room. Now he was pouring all his power on the
clergy. He shook his bony finger at the ministers and declared in ringing, stinging tones, "These men are the real
lawbreakers. The people passed a law and the preachers
persuaded the king to set it aside. These preachers have
failed in their duties. They have become enemies of the
people." No wonder he had wanted Uncle Patrick to stay
home!

And then, perhaps for the first time in America, Patrick
Henry declared out loud, "A government exists only by
the consent of the governed. The voice of the people is the
voice of God. A king who annuls a good law, instead of
being the father of his people, becomes a tyrant. He gives
up all rights to his people's obedience."

Peter Lyons jumped to his feet. "Your worships, the gentleman has spoken treason!"

Some of the richly dressed planters murmured, "Treason! Treason!"

But the flashing, overpowering flood of words had washed away the judges' reason. There was but one will in that room and it was the will of Patrick Henry. Colonel Henry forgot that he was supposed to be impartial. Tears he could not hide streamed down his face.

Mustering what dignity they could, the twenty clergymen rose and left the courthouse. They had had quite enough.

In his concluding remarks Mr. Lyons tried to salvage his case, but no one listened. The jury went out with Henry's bold phrases ringing in their ears. In less than five minutes, they were back. Verdict: one penny, as a token, for "damages."

The excited crowd clapped and cheered and stamped. They surged toward Patrick. In a one-hour speech he had become a popular hero. Wild with joy, they seized him and carried him on their shoulders around the courtyard. Sarah Henry, standing with her children on the courthouse porch, wiped her eyes and said, "You must always remember this day, the day your father made history in Hanover."

Patrick Coutts, Henry's first client, said, "Madam, I

would have given a considerable sum out of my own pocket rather than have my friend Patrick guilty of the crime he committed today. *Treason!*"

There were others who wondered about Patrick Henry's loyalties. His fiery words in the Parson's Case had shocked a colonial jury into taking a stand against the king of England. His speech had undermined the state church and questioned royal authority. Some said Patrick Henry was helping to loosen a chain of events that would lead to revolution.

chapter 6

Patrick Makes a New Friend

AS SOON as the Parson's Case was over, Patrick went to see the defendant, Reverend Maury.

"Mr. Maury," said Patrick with a smile, "if anything I said in court has harmed you, I am deeply sorry. I'm only a young lawyer, you know, trying to build up a practice and reputation."

The Reverend Maury exploded. "You are a scalawag, sir. For personal gain you have trampled underfoot the interests of religion, the rights of the church and the Crown itself. Your only consideration is popularity and I predict for you a disastrous future."

Somewhat shaken, but still determined to mend his fences, Patrick went to call on his uncle. The Reverend Patrick Henry gave his namesake a chilly welcome. "Well, young man, you won your case and I presume you are proud of yourself, but I do not share that opinion. When I meet my fellow clergymen, I find myself wishing you bore another name."

Patrick Henry was shocked. "Uncle," he said, "the clergy could have retained me on their side if they had wished, but they thought me unworthy. There is no moral rule which says I should refuse an honorable fee. A lawyer must live."

Patrick Henry had the temperament of a true lawyer. He was a good fighter but not a good hater. His imagination and sympathies were hotly kindled on the side of his client. During a case he spoke harsh words and dealt strong blows, but once the combat was over he felt no malice toward his opponent. It always surprised Pat when others did not return his friendliness.

After his success in the Parson's Case, Pat was known around Hanover as "the Greatest Orator of Nature." Fame did not change his habits. Sarah felt her husband's new importance and she urged him to acquire that badge of colonial distinction, a powdered wig, to wear on dress occasions. Pat just laughed. "I'll leave those trappings to the aristocrats. I'm still a flintlock-and-buckskin lad, Sarah, my dear."

One day Patrick looked up from his lawbooks to see one of the white-wigged aristocrats entering his office. Pat jumped to his feet. It was his old friend Colonel Nathaniel West Dandridge. "Patrick," said West Dandridge, "I come to you as a client. I want you to go to Williamsburg to plead a case for me. I am going to contest James Littlepage's election to the House of Burgesses. I believe Littlepage defeated me illegally, by saturating the voters with rum punch. Will you represent me in the case?"

Patrick looked down at his soiled leather breeches. Represent Colonel Dandridge?

"Why, sir, I'd be honored, but —"

The colonel thumped Pat on the back. "No buts, my boy. You've proved what you can do. We're all proud of you. Oh, by the way, little Dorothea sent you this. She heard about your success and wanted to make you a present." The colonel drew from his vest pocket a flannel penwiper stiched by his eight-year-old daughter. On the green felt cover she had embroidered in red the initials *P.H.* Patrick held it in his hand and looked at it. Then he carefully put it in his pocket.

"Thank you, sir. Tell Dolly I shall carry it for luck."

When Caesar brought Shandy to the door, for the trip to Williamsburg, he grinned at his master. "You're shore comin' up in the world, Mistah Patrick."

"Both of us are, Caesar. Where I go, you go."

"Yes, suh, that's the truth."

As Patrick cantered along the yellow leaf-strewn road, the fresh autumn wind whistled in his ears and reddened his cheeks. Just four years ago he journeyed to the capital to seek a lawyer's license; now he was returning to represent a rich and important client. He felt good all over. He hoped he would see Mr. George Wythe, Tom Jefferson's law teacher who refused to examine him. Deep within him,

Patrick felt the first faint stirring of ambition. One day he might really be somebody.

"The Greatest Orator of Nature" was a little surprised to find that his Hanover fame had not spread. Members of the House of Burgesses ignored the ill-dressed young stranger sauntering in the lobby of the capitol. Pat was to argue Colonel Dandridge's case before the Elections Committee of the House, men of importance like Peyton Randolph, Edmund Pendleton, and the great George Wythe. We know exactly how Patrick Henry was received by this committee because Judge John Tyler, the father of President Tyler, was there and he wrote it all down.

Any man possessing less firmness and independence of spirit than Mr. Henry [Tyler wrote] would have been discouraged by the proud airs of the aristocrats. He was ushered with great state and ceremony into the room of the committee. Mr. Henry was dressed in very coarse apparel, no one knew anything of him, and scarcely was he treated with decent respect by any one except the chairman, Richard Bland. But the general contempt was soon changed into general admiration, for Mr. Henry distinguished himself by a brilliant argument. Such a burst of eloquence from a man so very plain and ordinary in appearance struck the committee with amazement, so that a deep and perfect silence took place during the speech, and not a sound but from his lips was to be heard in the room.

At the conclusion of the case, Mr. Wythe approached Patrick. George Wythe was a short, slender man whose high forehead and sharp nose made him look like an owl. His head, somewhat large for his body, was said to be filled with the wisdom of the ages. Patrick felt his self-confidence oozing away.

"Mr. Henry." A dry smile cracked the parchment of George Wythe's face. "Mr. Henry, I want you to know I do not hold against you your lack of education. I myself was born in Back River, Virginia, and had little schooling. My blessed mother was my tutor. Today, sir, your lack of learning was not apparent. You spoke with surprising skill." Mr. Wythe made a courtly bow and departed. Patrick suddenly felt eight feet tall.

Despite Patrick's stirring plea, Colonel Dandridge lost his claim. Lawyer Henry lost his case, but he had displayed his talent before some of the leading men in the colony. The time had been well spent.

As Patrick rode back to Hanover, his thoughts did not dwell on his defeat. Defeat he was used to, and West Dandridge could well afford another campaign for the

House of Burgesses. Pat's head was buzzing with the talk
he had heard in Williamsburg. Every place he had gone
— to the H-shaped capitol on business, to the Raleigh
Tavern for a glass of punch, to William and Mary College
to see Tom Jefferson — everywhere just one subject was
discussed: "The Stamp Act . . . the Stamp Act . . . the
Stamp Act."

King George III, although muddleheaded and weak,
made himself felt in America. His mother, the Princess
Dowager, stood at his elbow saying, "Be King, George, be
King." George did his best to obey. To America's misfor-
tune, he ran things to suit himself. England needed
money, so His Royal Majesty decided to tax the Americans at every turn. He and his shortsighted minister,
George Grenville, concocted the Stamp Tax which required tax stamps on "every skin or piece of paper" used
in the colonies. This meant that all newspapers, pamph-
lets, deeds, licenses, wills, contracts and diplomas were
taxed. Taxes were even placed on every pack of cards and
pair of dice in America, and there were a lot of those. To
make matters worse, King George planned to use part of
the stamp tax revenue to keep twenty thousand British
troops in America to control the colonies! Insult added to
injury.

A few Britishers realized the folly of this plan. "An
Englishman," protested Edmund Burke, "is the unfittest

person on earth to argue another Englishman into slavery." But "Be-a-King-George" turned a deaf ear, and the hated Stamp Act became law. Benjamin Franklin, who was in London trying to prevent the passage of the bill, wrote home, "We might as well have hindered the sun's setting." The American colonies were staggered by the blow.

Back in Hanover, Patrick went to consult his father. "Sir," said Pat, "do you believe the English have the right to lay taxes on us, when we have no representative in Parliament?"

Judge Henry cleared his throat. "Patrick, you know the Stamp Act has passed. It is now the law of the land. It's too late for discussion."

"But, Father," cried Patrick, "are we to submit in silence to such unfair treatment? If a government is good, it must rest on the *consent* of the governed. The American colonies have been denied —"

"Son," Judge Henry interrupted sternly, "I consider myself more Scottish than English, but even to me your talk is shockingly disloyal. We will terminate our conversation." To have his own father speak this way appalled Patrick. They had always been able to talk things over.

Judge Henry was not the only one in Hanover who found Patrick's tirades against the Stamp Act distasteful.

Some of Pat's old friends began to avoid him. Was it not dangerous to blast the British law that way?

"Sarah," said Patrick, "pack up our things. We are moving to Louisa County. I think I'll be happier on the frontier. It is getting a little stuffy here." Danger from Indians was better than silent inaction.

Sarah, always obedient and submissive to her adored Patrick, did just as she was told, although she was not eager to move so far away from all the Sheltons. The Henrys loaded their possessions into wagon and carriage and moved west over rocky and stump-strewn roads to Roundabout Plantation.

Roundabout was a simple story-and-a-half white wooden house, with three rooms downstairs and one above. Behind the house were several small outbuildings where the slaves lived and labored at everything from candle dripping to harness making. The seven Henrys and their slaves settled down in the back-country solitude that made the village of Hanover seem like a city.

Patrick liked being a backwoodsman. From his front door he looked out on the sleepy valley of Roundabout Creek and the rolling fields and forests beyond. It was a peaceful, lonely vista. Roundabout was nine miles from Louisa Courthouse where Pat practiced law. He took his gun with him when he rode to court and often killed deer or pheasant along the way. Sometimes he would vanish for several days and go hunting, camping at night in the forests. When he returned, still dressed in his greasy leather hunting clothes, he would stride into the courtroom with his saddlebags on his arm, and take up the first of his cases that was called.

The pioneers and farmers of Louisa County loved him. They looked on him as a hero. When a vacancy occurred in the House of Burgesses, they promptly elected Patrick Henry delegate from Louisa County. Louisa was a hotbed of frontier independence and Presbyterian revolt. The people knew Pat had defied the powers-that-be in the Parson's Case and they hoped he would do it again.

It was spring when Burgess Patrick Henry returned to Williamsburg. The yellow-green weeping willows dipped over yellow jonquils and purple hyacinths in well-tended gardens. Pat marveled at the sights as he walked along the brick paths with his lanky young friend Tom Jefferson.

"This must be the most beautiful town in the world, Tom."

"Oh, there's absolutely no place like Williamsburg in the springtime," Tom agreed.

People turned to look at the two friends strolling beneath the elms and sycamores on Duke of Gloucester Street. They were an oddly matched pair. Tom, twenty-

two years old, tall and graceful and elegantly dressed;
Patrick, twenty-eight, a lean, spare figure who ambled
along stooping slightly and gawking at everything.

A coach drawn by six prancing horses in gorgeous
trappings rattled past. It was escorted by richly dressed
footmen and on the door was the royal coat of arms.
Inside the coach rode a white-wigged gentleman gor-
geously dressed in scarlet and gold.

"What in the name of thunder?" gasped Pat.

"That's only the governor," laughed Jefferson. "Francis
Fauquier, a good friend of mine. He's the gayest blade in
Virginia; gambles furiously, dances like a madman, and
loves music. I go to the palace regularly to play trios
with him. You must bring your fiddle and go with me.
Right now we're working up some splended new music by
Bach."

"Can the governor play 'Flies in the Buttermilk'?" Pat
grinned. "That's more my style. You know, Tom, I'm not
easily cowed, but when I think of myself walking into the
House of Burgesses tomorrow as a *delegate*, I almost
shiver in my shoes. Fancy me, one of the 'Qo'hees' from
the back country, sitting down to make laws with all those
'Tuckahoes,' all those rich aristocrats from Tidewater.
When I think of hobnobbing with the Lees, the Carters,
the Pendletons, the Pages and the Randolphs, my blood
runs cold. And as for Mr. George Wythe!"

"Never mind," said Tom. "They are a formidable bunch, but there's one you can count on. His manner is easy and noble. He's tall, erect and graceful. He's a natural athlete and the best horseman in America. He's very quiet but he's so strong I've seen him crumble a walnut between his fingers. He's —"

"Hold on, Tom! Who is this marvel?"

"George Washington. You'll like him."

Next day when Patrick Henry entered the chamber of the House of Burgesses, he stood still and looked about in awe. Here the first representative assembly in America had been meeting for over one hundred and forty years. Patrick's sharp eyes took in every detail of the impressive room: the white walls paneled with black walnut, the deeply recessed, many-paned windows filtering the sunlight, and the double rows of straight-backed benches facing each other on either side of the room. At the end of the building, where the wall was curved, there were three round windows and beneath them stood the high-backed Speaker's armchair. It was a beautiful room.

A tall man dressed in a red-coated uniform hurried toward Pat. When they shook hands his big brown fist almost pulverized Pat's bones. "I'm George Washington. Young Tom Jefferson told me to look out for you, Mr. Henry." Patrick swallowed. Washington was one of the great men of Virginia. Everyone knew his reputation for

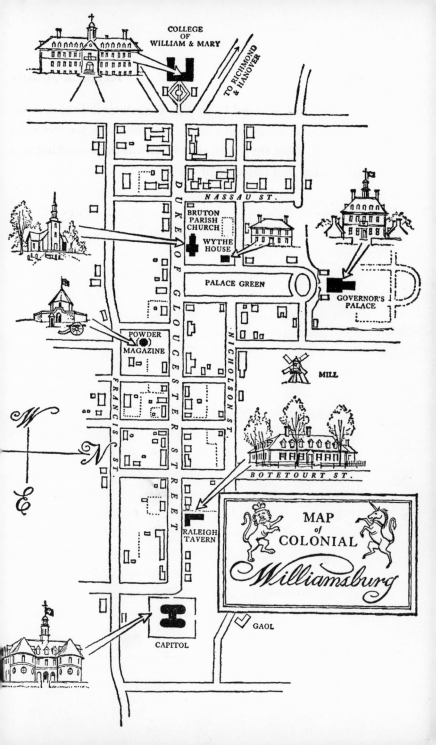

COLLEGE
OF
WILLIAM & MARY

TO RICHMOND & HANOVER

NASSAU ST.

BRUTON PARISH CHURCH

WYTHE HOUSE

PALACE GREEN

GOVERNOR'S PALACE

DUKE OF GLOUCESTER STREET

NICHOLSON ST.

POWDER MAGAZINE

MILL

FRANCIS ST.

BOTETOURT ST.

RALEIGH TAVERN

MAP
of
COLONIAL
Williamsburg

GAOL

CAPITOL

bravery and leadership in the French and Indian War.

The two men looked each other straight in the eye for a moment. Then they both smiled. It was the beginning of a friendship that lasted until death.

chapter 7

"Treason! Treason!"

PATRICK HENRY had been a member of the House of Burgesses exactly nine days when he rocked that dignified body to its foundations. It happened on Wednesday, May 29, 1765, his twenty-ninth birthday. That date marked a turning point for the delegate from Louisa County and for the crown colony of Virginia. The political climate of Williamsburg was never the same again.

The month-long session of the House was drawing to a close. Many members had already gone home to look after the spring crops. On that warm May day only thirty-nine of the one hundred and sixteen Burgesses gathered for the meeting.

As Patrick strode along the diagonal path to the capitol he glanced up at the British flag on top of the clock tower. A faint breeze stirred the red and blue Union Jack. He wondered just how strong Virginia's loyalty was to that flag.

Pat stopped a moment to admire the gnarled paper mulberry trees near the capitol. He was never able to ignore the beauties of nature. A richly dressed gentleman in a bottle-green velvet coat stopped beside him. It was Edmund Pendleton, the acknowledged leader of the House. Pendleton was only fifteen years older than Patrick, but his white wig and stately manner made him seem elderly.

"Beautiful morning, eh, Mr. Henry? I've seldom heard a greater variety of bird calls."

"Oh, sir, you should let me take you to the wild woods of Louisa County. There's where the birds abound." Abruptly, Patrick changed the subject. "Sir, will the Stamp Tax be brought up today for discussion?"

"Its passage will be noted. Beyond that, there is little one can do."

"Little one can do? The British force us to pay a tax on every piece of paper used in the colonies, and *there is little one can do?*"

"The Stamp Tax is now the law of the land, Mr. Henry." Pendleton spoke the words crisply. He bowed formally and departed. It was clear he did not care to discuss the matter with the upstart from Louisa. Like most colonists, Edmund Pendleton felt helpless before the hated Stamp Act. Throughout America there was panic and despair, but little hope that the British government could be resisted.

Patrick recalled Tom Jefferson's remarks about the imposing Edmund Pendleton. "Taken all in all," Jefferson said, "Mr. Pendleton is the ablest man in debate I ever met. He is cool, smooth and persuasive. His language is flow-ing, his ideas acute." Here was a leader to reckon with.

Patrick hurried through the groups of delegates chatting and laughing in the east wing of the capitol. The man he looked for was not hard to find. He was the tallest man in the room.

"Colonel Washington, at last I've found you!" Pat looked about, then lowered his voice. "Will you help me attack the Stamp Act today?"

"Ah, Mr. Henry, you didn't know that I never speak in public? People accuse me of being active in the field, but silent in the House. I'm afraid it is all too true."

Patrick regarded the tall, muscular man in astonishment. Washington was not handsome, but he was impressive. His large nose, high cheekbones, and alert blue-gray eyes gave him the look of an eagle. Colonel Washington — the hero who had been cited in this very capitol for his "brave and steady behavior" in the French and Indian War — was timid about making a speech. Incredible!

"Some people," Washington continued, "say there is nothing wrong with the Stamp Act. They argue that the tax money will be spent to defend and protect the colonies. Even James Otis and Benjamin Franklin do not object to it."

"They will," said Henry, narrowing his blue eyes, "but if they don't, I am neither Otis nor Franklin. I am Patrick Henry, Burgess from Louisa County, and I do object. If we need an army we can pay for it ourselves. Colonel, America has never known anything like this before. The Stamp Tax will hit rich and poor, old and young, great and small. Money from every American man, woman, and child will drain into the rich British treasury. And, moreover, no American had a chance to vote on this blasted act. Here is ruthless taxation without consent of those who are taxed."

"By heaven, Mr. Henry," Washington's voice took on the ring of steel, "I agree with you. I have not the talent to speak on the subject, but I am sure my neighbor and attorney, George Johnston, will do so. He is a man of character and a champion of liberty. I'll speak to him at once."

The two men grasped hands. They understood one another.

John Robinson, the genial Speaker of the House, seated himself in his paneled-back chair and called the meeting to order. The Burgesses on the benches before him were an oddly assorted lot. Some were in velvet dress with ruffles and powdered hair. Others wore rough cloth and buckskin. The Tuckahoes, the landed gentry from Tidewater Virginia, took for granted their control of the legislature. True, there were more upcountry members now, but they were inarticulate and lacked leadership. The Tuckahoes had never been seriously challenged.

George Johnston of Fairfax County rose from his seat.

"Mr. Speaker, with your permission, sir, I move that the House go into the Committee of the Whole to consider the Stamp Act."

Patrick Henry jumped up. "I second the motion."

There was a slight stir of excitement. Consider the Stamp Act? Could one discuss the pros and cons of a law already passed by the British Parliament?

A vote was taken and the motion carried. The Clerk of the House placed the Speaker's silver mace under the table. Speaker Robinson left his seat and Peyton Randolph, the Attorney General of Virginia, replaced him as presiding officer. Randolph, large and elegant, presided with heavy dignity. It was the Randolph estate, Tuckahoe, that gave the conservative aristocrats their nickname.

Patrick Henry longed to take the floor at once, but he knew it was proper to let the established leaders speak first. A new member must wait his turn. One by one the elegantly dressed gentlemen rose to make tame, dignified comments on the Stamp Act. Lifelong obedience to the king of England kept them from radical thoughts. Virginia had, after all, been an English colony for over one hundred and fifty years. As Patrick listened, he slumped in his seat.

"Let us send another memorial to the king and ask him to reconsider," said Edmund Pendleton.

"May I remind you," said George Wythe, his dark gray

eyes snapping, "that Mr. Lee and I drew up resolutions of protest last November, which the king ignored? What attention would he pay to protests made at this late date? Even the Massachusetts patriot, James Otis, says publicly: 'It is our duty humbly and silently to accept the decisions of Parliament.'"

Patrick Henry stared down at his sturdy boots. Virginia could *not* submit without protest. It was unthinkable. Slowly and thoughtfully he got to his feet. For a few moments he said nothing. He glanced from one member to another. All eyes were fastened on him. Hesitant and awkward, he looked exactly what his drawling accent and plain dress proclaimed him — a member from the country, out of place with men of the world.

"Gentlemen," Henry began in a low voice, "the Stamp Tax is going to invade every inch of American life. Picture with me the buckskin bridegroom." Patrick crooked his arm and, with a dreamy expression, took a few steps as though leading a bride down an aisle. Then he turned toward his "bride" and pretended to pull a ring from his pocket. He bent forward, as though he were about to slip the ring on her finger. His pantomime riveted the Burgesses' attention.

"With this ring, I thee —" Pat stopped. A look of dismay spread across his face. "The stamp!" he cried in mock horror. "I forgot the stamp!" Hastily he pretended to dig a stamp from his pocket, lick it and stick it on an invisible license. Then Pat's fine white teeth flashed in a broad smile and he said lovingly, "With this stamp, I thee wed."

Loud laughter rang through the House. Patrick Henry, actor, had captivated his audience. He bowed his head and let the merriment subside. When the room was utterly quiet, Patrick Henry, orator, spoke. His manner was no longer hesitant but self-possessed.

"Gentlemen, the Stamp Act has been forced upon us by a 'sick' king — I understand in Williamsburg it is considered ill-mannered to refer to King George's fits of insanity in plain words — by a 'sick' king, and his weak minister George Grenville. This act is, in my humble opinion, illegal, unconstitutional and unjust."

The Burgesses stirred nervously. What kind of blunt talk was this?

Patrick Henry opened an old lawbook he held in his hand. "Gentlemen, I have written some resolutions which I respectfully submit to you." With a mounting sense of drama he read aloud the sentences he had jotted on the flyleaf of his book. Not a sound broke the increasing tension in the room.

Patrick had composed seven resolutions. They were simple, clear, defiant.

One — Resolved: That the first settlers in this country brought with them all privileges enjoyed by the people of Great Britain.

Two — Resolved: That these privileges have been confirmed by two royal charters.

Three — Resolved: That self-taxation is the cornerstone of British freedom.

Four — Resolved: That Virginia's right to self-government and self-taxation has been constantly recognized by the kings and the people of Great Britain.

Five — Resolved: That the Virginia assembly has the sole right and power to lay taxes on this colony.

Six — Resolved: That Virginians are not bound to obey any law other than those passed by their own assembly.

Seven — Resolved: That any person who speaks to the contrary shall be considered an enemy of the colony.

Patrick Henry snapped his lawbook shut. He glared around him defiantly, and sat down. All that he had done was to attempt to take the leadership of the colony on the most momentous question of the day.

The stillness that precedes a storm gripped the room. Then a clamor of excitement broke loose. In the words of Thomas Jefferson, who was watching with other students from the doorway, "There followed a most bloody debate." The proud leaders of the House, John Robinson,

Peyton Randolph, Edmund Pendleton, George Wythe, and Richard Bland rose one by one to denounce Patrick Henry and his incredible resolutions. In red-faced fury they hurled acid words at him. How *dare* he place Virginia's lawmaking power above the British Parliament!

Their phrases stung. "The upcountry clown" . . . "The talkative young actor from Louisa" . . . "Our buckskin bumpkin orator." The conservatives delivered their bitter insults with exaggerated politeness. Their threats and abuse angered Patrick. Once again he took the floor. Now he was thoroughly aroused. His head was high. His deep-set eyes blazed. His rich voice sent chills through his listeners. As he spoke, Burgesses leaned forward. Their breath came faster, as if they were on a mountain peak. They were listening to one of the world's great orations.

"Caesar had his Brutus," Patrick thundered in conclusion, "Charles the First his Cromwell, and George the Third —"

"Treason!" shouted Speaker Robinson.

"Treason! Treason!" yelled the followers of the king, jumping to their feet.

Henry paused dramatically. For a moment the Burgesses seemed frozen in place. Then with great presence of mind, Patrick Henry finished the sentence and baffled his accusers. Stressing each word, he said slowly, "And

George the Third may profit by their example. *If this be treason, make the most of it.*"

Tom Jefferson almost cheered aloud. "It was a splendid display," he wrote later. "Patrick Henry's talents are such as I have never heard from any other man. He spoke as Homer wrote, with torrents of eloquence."

The time had come to vote on Henry's radical resolutions. It was clear the delegates from the western part of the colony would follow Henry against the eastern aristocrats. The "High-Blooded Colts," as Pat and his followers were called, met the "Old Field Nags," the cool conservatives, head on.

The count was taken. Patrick Henry won his resolutions—by one vote. Pat looked toward Tom Jefferson in the doorway and saw a broad smile of congratulation spread across his face.

Peyton Randolph rose and strode angrily out of the room, muttering between clenched teeth, "By heaven, I would have given five hundred guineas for a single vote!" The others who had voted against Henry stalked out indignantly.

Richard Henry Lee, George Johnston, and the rest of the High-Blooded Colts gathered around Patrick to congratulate him. The hubbub subsided when the dignified figure of Colonel Washington approached. Washington,

broad-shouldered, neat-waisted, and straight as an Indian, walked toward Patrick. He held out his hand and said in a voice everyone in the room could hear, "Mr. Henry, to-day you have put Virginia first in the colonies."

chapter 8

The Stamp Act Song

"HOW the devil did you dare, Pat?"

"Dare what, Uncle Langloo?"

"Dare make that danged treason-smelling speech everybody's talkin' about."

The two were sitting on the steps of Roundabout Plantation enjoying a rosy June sunset. Uncle Langloo's question brought a grin to Pat's face.

"Well, sir," said Patrick. "I was convinced my cause was right. And if my words proved too hot, I was well acquainted with the backwoods. I could count on a safe retreat."

"Son, you shore shook them critters up. I heard that only a fistful showed up at the governor's palace for the king's birthday ball. Francis Fauquier is the most popular governor Virginia ever got, but what you said, Pat, fired up a revolt."

"Hush, Uncle Langloo, I hear a quail." Patrick was not the kind to dwell on his triumphs. Over the darkening meadows came a faint "Bob-bob white, bob-bob white." "One of the most beautiful sounds I know, Uncle Langloo. It always makes my heart skip a beat."

"Always makes my mouth water," said Langloo. "Hot quail and cold ale — nuthin's better. I got me a covey of quail 'tother day over on Three Chopt Road. Quail on toast—delicious!"

"Every time I hit Three Chopt," Patrick said wistfully, "I long to head west and keep going." Three Chopt Road was a forest trail that led from tidewater westward to the Rivanna River. Scouts and hunters had marked it out by slashing triple ax marks on tree trunks along the way. "There's a whole continent out there just waiting to be explored. I can feel it beckoning. I'd like to take to the trail and live like an Indian."

"Leave exploring to fellows like Langloo Winston and Daniel Boone, m' boy. You stay right here and keep them British stirred up. You got a gift for it."

"Don't know about that, Uncle Langloo, but somebody has to stand up to them, or they'll tax us to poverty."

" 'S a fact. Say, have you heard the Stamp Act Song? They sing it in all the taverns now. Kind of catchy." Langloo threw back his head and lifted his cracked voice in song. He made Patrick think of a hound dog with a sore throat.

> "With the beasts of the wood
> We will ramble for food
> And lodge in wild deserts and caves

And live poor as Job
On the skirts of the globe
Before we'll submit to be slaves."

Patrick Henry's Stamp Act Resolutions had indeed
stirred up the British. Governor Fauquier reported to His
Majesty's government in London that "very shocking and
indecent language was used in the debates by a Mr. Henry,
a young lawyer who had not been a month a member of
the House. He overpowered the young, hot and giddy
members. Things might have been different," the Governor added apologetically, "if more Burgesses had done
their duty and stayed until the end of the session."

What to the British was "shocking and indecent language" was to the Americans a trumpet call for action. At
first the Virginia Resolutions were handed secretly from
colony to colony. Some men were afraid to be caught
reading the bold words, much less publishing them. But
once they reached New England, they were printed far
and wide. Virginia was the largest, the oldest, the most
important colony in America, and Virginia had spoken.
The Boston *Gazette* reported that an old patriot named
Oxenbridge Thacher lifted himself from his deathbed and
cried aloud, "Oh! Those Virginians are men! They are
noble spirits!"

Henry's words flamed and crackled up and down the

eastern seaboard. "The people's spirits took fire," John Adams said, "and burst forth in a blaze." The resistance was bloody. A network of patriot clubs called the Sons of Liberty sent mobs to terrorize supporters of the British. They burned stamps and hanged tax collectors in effigy.

In protest against the dreaded stamps, business everywhere stopped. When it resumed, the stamps were ignored. The colonists were in open revolt. General Gage, the British commander in America, grew alarmed. "The Virginia Resolves," he told his home office, "have given the signal for a general outcry over the continent."

Patrick Henry had expressed what thousands of Americans thought, but dared not say. As the other colonies took their place beside Virginia, the forces that shattered the British empire were, for the first time, clearly joined.

Many Americans disagreed with the rebels. John Randolph, the elegant Tory squire of Tuckahoe, apologized for Virginia's folly. Benjamin Franklin, the diplomatic and patient sage of Philadelphia, who was in London trying to promote peace, expressed amazement at the rashness of the Virginia assembly. "We must maintain firm loyalty to the Crown," Franklin stated, "whatever the madness of the blind populace."

Some Tories in Virginia even made threats on Patrick Henry's life. A Frenchman, visiting Hanover that June, recorded in his diary:

In every tavern nothing is discussed but the stamp duties. One man said he'd sooner die than pay a farthing. A great deal is said about the noble patriot, Mr. Henry, who lives in this county. Men say publicly if the least injury is offered him, they'd stand by him to the last drop of their blood. Some mutter betwixt their teeth, let the worst come to the worst, we'll call the French to our aid.

No one really expected words and riots to repeal the Stamp Act, but the Americans held an ace which they played with a vengeance: boycott. The colonists turned their backs on British goods. British export trade dwindled to a halt. The English merchants were irate.

Benjamin Franklin was busy in London buttonholing members of Parliament and urging repeal of the Stamp Act. Leaders in the House of Commons examined Franklin at length on the reaction to the Stamp Act in America. He won great praise for his answers.

A friendly member helped Franklin sound a clear warning to the British. "What," he asked, "used to be the pride of the Americans?"

"To indulge in the fashions and manufactures of Great Britain," answered Franklin.

"What is now their pride?"

"To wear their old clothes over again, till they can make new ones."

Feeling ran high in London. It was evident something had to be done. Prime Minister Grenville called for an army to enforce the Stamp Act. He did not seem to care that it would cost more to collect the tax than the tax was worth. Benjamin Franklin remarked, "Whenever an Englishman hears of discontent in the colonies, he cries, 'Send over an army or a fleet and reduce the dogs to *reason.*'"

England's greatest orator, William Pitt, sick with gout, left his bed to speak in behalf of America. Pitt loved the Americans for their British independence of spirit. For the second time within a year, the Stamp Act crisis brought forth a great speech, this one in the House of Commons.

"I rejoice that America has resisted," said Pitt. "I ask *who* has represented an American here? The Americans have been driven to madness by injustice. Will you punish them for the madness you have caused? There are two lines in a ballad of a man's behavior to his wife that apply to you and your colonies:

> 'Be to her faults a little blind,
> Be to her virtues very kind.'

The Americans have a God-given right to tax themselves." And then William Pitt handed the Americans their battle cry. "My position is this. I will maintain it to my last hour: *no taxation without representation.*"

Just as Patrick Henry's eloquence fired the colonists to resist the Stamp Act, William Pitt's eloquence turned the tide in Britain. On March 18, 1766, Parliament repealed the monstrous Stamp Act. It had been in effect only one year but had wrought great damage. There was rejoicing in London, where everyone suffered from the drying up of American trade. Bells rang through the city. Ships on the Thames displayed their colors and torches illuminated the streets.

When the news finally reached America, another celebration was touched off. Fireworks exploded and bands played. The colonists drank toasts to William Pitt and King George III and the New York assembly voted to erect statues to both of them. Harmony seemed restored, although Great Britain still insisted it had the right to tax the Americans.

Patrick Henry, now a continental celebrity, was re-elected to the House of Burgesses. Virginia's upcountry citizens would never want another candidate so long as he lived. He personified their rough and ready ideal of liberty.

The first person Patrick saw when he returned to the House was a tall young man with reddish hair.

"Tom Jefferson! What are you doing here? Observing again? You'll soon be able to write a book about this legislature."

"Not observing, Pat," Jefferson said with an engaging smile. "Legislating."

"You're a delegate?"

"The representative from Albemarle County, at your service, sir." Jefferson made a courtly bow.

"Capital!" Patrick regarded his friend. Tall and thin with tawny skin and hair, Tom had an independent half-tossing way of carrying his head. He looked every inch the intelligent aristocrat. His radical idealism did not show.

"I hope I can be a help to you, Pat," Tom said with some shyness. His admiration of Henry was unlimited.

"You'll make a great ally. We'll heat up those cold conservatives. You do the writing and I'll do the talking. We'll work together like thumb and forefinger."

"I've a message for you, Pat, from Reverend Maury, my old teacher."

"My old enemy. He gave me a terrible blast after the Parson's Case."

"Oh, he has come over to your side."

"What?"

"Your Stamp Act speech persuaded him you are not a scoundrel but a true patriot."

"It used to be an insult to call a man a patriot. In England, a patriot is someone who wants to overthrow the government."

"To me," said Jefferson, "a patriot is a man who gives his first love and loyalty to the land of his birth. It's an American rather than an English word, Pat, and you're a perfect example of it." Many people thought Thomas Jefferson chilly and austere, but Henry seemed to thaw him out.

"Have you met the new governor, Lord Botetourt?" Jefferson asked.

"Not yet. I hear he is short, fat and cheerful." Patrick laughed.

"My cousin John Randolph went to call on him. John says Botetourt wore a silk coat but had two or three holes in his stockings. The governor is a bachelor. I'll never get over missing the Fauquiers."

Jefferson's good friend, the gifted and popular Governor Francis Fauquier, who did so much for the social and intellectual life of Williamsburg, had lost a long struggle with illness. His death grieved the colonists. They buried him with every honor the capital could give. Fauquier's body lies beneath the stone floor of Bruton Parish Church. Inscribed on a marble marker are these words:

The Hon. Francis Fauquier, Esq.

Lt. Governor and Commander-in-Chief of the colony over which he presided near 10 years, much to his own honor and the ease and satisfaction of the inhabitants. He was a gentleman of the most amiable disposition, generous, just and mild, and possessed in an eminent degree of all the social virtues.

If ever virtue lost a friend sincere,
If ever sorrow claimed Virginia's tear,
If ever death a noble conquest made,
'Twas when Fauquier the debt of nature paid.

The new governor, Lord Botetourt, arrived in Williamsburg in regal splendor. Six snow-white horses drew the handsome cream and gold coach of state he had brought with him from England. Patrick Henry and Thomas Jefferson were present when Botetourt entered the Council Chamber for the first time. He was richly dressed in a light red coat shot through with gold thread.

Lord Botetourt made an elaborate speech about King George's love of his subjects. Many of the Burgesses were impressed. Henry and Jefferson were not. Afterward the two friends repaired to the Raleigh Tavern for a spot of tea.

"Well, what did you think?" asked Patrick.

"He speaks very slowly and with long pauses, just like George the Third," said Tom.

"That speech was calculated to flatter Virginia and strengthen our ties to Britain."

"He seems amiable and eager to please. Perhaps he'll be good for Virginia."

"I doubt it." Patrick took a long drink of the hot tea. "The more I see of English rule, the more I think that what's good for Virginia is *Virginians*."

chapter 9

"Champagne Charlie"

"SARAH," said Patrick. "We've come up in the world. I think it's time we acquired a country seat."

"Patrick, you're not going to buy more land, are you?"

"Not going to, *have*. I signed the deed last night for Scotchtown."

Sarah gasped. "You mean the big old place in Hanover? Patrick, we can't be that important."

"Well, it's ours and we must get used to our lordly estate. I'm not very superstitious, but I hope Scotchtown will bring us better luck than it did poor old Colonel Chiswell who built it."

"What happened to him?"

"That hotheaded Scot stabbed a man to death in a quarrel and then committed suicide. Unfortunately, the only man I want to do away with is in England where I can't get my hands on him. How I would enjoy taking a stab at Charlie Townshend."

"Pat!" Sarah was shocked. She had been married to this man for seventeen years but she still could not tell when he was serious. "You *wouldn't!*"

Patrick leaned down and gave his pretty wife a kiss.

"Not if you don't want me to. For your sake, Sarah, I'll let Champagne Charlie go on living."

Charles Townshend, the most glittering jewel in the Tory party, was heartily hated by all the Americans. As Chancellor of the Exchequer, he was now threatening new and stronger taxes for the American colonies. This was a sure way to gain popularity in England, where the upper classes were being smothered by taxation. Anything that lessened taxes at home was considered sensational by the English voters.

Charles Townshend's watchword was popularity. He was one of the flashiest politicians in England and his wit and charm made him much sought after in society. A great party-goer, he was christened Champagne Charlie after he made a witty and reckless speech in the House while he was intoxicated.

It was pouring rain when Patrick drove his family up the muddy red road to Scotchtown, their new home. Rain did not dampen spirits inside the chaise. Excitement fairly crackled in the air. Sarah was silent, but the six children were exploding with anticipation.

"How old is the house, Papa?" asked Patsy.

"Over fifty years. Some say Chiswell copied it after his in-laws' estate, Tuckahoe. He married a Randolph, you know. Scotchtown is used to aristocrats. Now you will all have to behave like little ladies and gentlemen."

Everyone shouted with laughter. The Henry children were not parlor-bred. They were used to running through the fields and forests, as wild as young deer.

"I see it! I see it!" In her eagerness little Anne almost fell out of the carriage.

Scotchtown loomed up on a broad-topped hill before them. The beautiful sixteen-room mansion looked out over rolling, fertile countryside. Today when you visit Scotchtown it seems small for a mansion, but in those days it was considered one.

"How much land do we own, Papa?" John, an outdoor man like his father, seemed much older than his fourteen years.

"Almost a thousand acres," said Patrick, "and wild game on every foot of it. We'll have some great hunting here, John."

Caesar trotted his horse up to the carriage. He leaned over and called, "Mistah Pat, Dicy say she cain't live at Scotchtown."

"What in heaven is she talking about?"

"She say this here place is haunted. She say the Chiswell spooks roam round at night and give folks the chilly creeps." Caesar laughed, but not very heartily.

"You tell that good-for-nothing girl to hold her tongue. I never want to hear another word about ghosts — especially in front of the children. You ought to know better."

Patrick spoke sternly, something he never did with Caesar.

"Yes, *suh!*" Caesar departed quickly.

"Ghosts?" the children said, hopefully.

"Nonsense," Patrick said, flatly.

The carriage rattled into the center of a courtyard. Clustered around the curving driveway were many small houses. "So many outbuildings! What are they all for, Pat?" It was the first time Sarah had spoken on the trip.

"Well, that one's the kitchen. Behind it is the washhouse. There's the warehouse, the plantation store, the schoolhouse, the blacksmith shop, the boys' bunkhouse, the smokehouse and the overseer's office. Yonder are the slaves' quarters. We've enough cabins to house thirty slaves and we'll need that many to keep this place going."

"How can we afford all this?" Sarah was the only worrier in the family.

"My law practice is booming, dear one, and I've been buying up land and reselling it for some time now. If a man keeps his wits about him, there's a lot of money to be made these days. Land I got for almost nothing, a few years ago, sells for a pretty penny right now."

"This place looks immense to me." Sarah spoke in a small voice.

"You haven't seen anything yet," Patrick said proudly. "We even own a mill up on New Found River. We're the landed gentry now, Sarah. Children!" Patrick called.

"Come look at our handsome oak. You don't see a tree like that every day. I christen thee . . . the Henry Oak." Pat let his great voice roll out the words. The children cheered.

Patrick lifted Sarah and carried her gently up the ten red stone steps and into the large center hall of their new home. It was not just a sentimental gesture. Sarah suffered increasingly from a strange sickness. The real reason Patrick Henry bought Scotchtown was to try to improve his wife's ailing health.

"Oh, Pat, look at the lovely walnut paneling! And the corner fireplaces! And the black marble mantels!" Sarah suddenly sounded like a girl again. It gladdened Patrick's heart. Ever since little Neddy's birth, she had been given to long periods of moody silence. He hoped that becoming the mistress of one of the great houses of Hanover would renew her spirit.

Billy raced through the doorway. "Papa, Papa, there's a dungeon downstairs. It has iron bars and everything!"

Patsy called from the back of the hallway. "Come quickly, I found a secret staircase!" The family trooped up the rough stairs after her. To their surprise, they discovered an enormous attic room covered the entire house.

"What fun we'll have here," exclaimed Patsy, who inherited Patrick's enthusiasm. "Dances, and house parties and —"

"Whoa, Patsy," said her father. "You'd better take your bonnet off before you start to entertain."

At first, Scotchtown was indeed a happy home for the Henrys. Patrick Henry thought the most important thing in a child's life was a strong, healthy body. He encouraged his six children to be as free as the birds. The Henrys were eight years old before their father allowed them to wear shoes. They were nine or ten before they received any schooling.

One day Uncle Patrick drove over from Slash Church to call on the new squire of Scotchtown. The Reverend Patrick Henry greeted his namesake with a scolding. "Patrick, there is a swarm of children running around out there, some black, some white. They are bareheaded, barefooted, halloing and whooping in every direction, rough as nature left them. Is this the way to bring up children?"

"In a word, yes."

"I do not understand you. Why aren't those wild animals in school?"

"I believe young children should live with nature and learn from it, Uncle."

"Nonsense. You're careless about their education because you were careless about your own. The sins of the father are visited upon the children." Uncle Patrick folded his hands on his black coat. He could look extremely pious.

Patrick threw back his head and laughed. "Come sit by the fire, Uncle, and have a glass of port. It's a chilly day for April."

The two men were no sooner seated in the large armchairs near the crackling hearth than Pat started talking politics. His uncle was a valuable source of London news and news was hard to come by in the country. "Tell me what the Bishop writes about William Pitt. Pitt's health is vital to America, I think. He and Edmund Burke are the only men in the House of Commons who understand us."

"Brace yourself for a shock, Patrick. Pitt, the Great Commoner, is no longer in the House of Commons."

"What do you mean?"

"King George brought him back as Prime Minister and made him a peer. William Pitt is now Lord Chatham of the House of Lords. They say he is as delighted as a child by the king's flattery."

"Zounds!" cried Patrick. "Imagine Pitt sinking into the peerage! That will chill his popularity in America."

"I'm afraid sinking is all too apt a word. You know he suffers from gout and now he is beginning to show unmistakable signs of insanity. It is whispered that a bungling doctor checked Pitt's gout and threw it upon his nerves."

Patrick held his head in his hands. Perhaps because Henry was a rugged, plain man from the provinces, he was fascinated by Pitt, the complex, sophisticated English leader. Both men were far-seeing patriots who moved others to action by their dramatic oratory.

"You haven't heard the worst," said Uncle Patrick, calmly refilling his long clay pipe. "As soon as Pitt went to Bath for treatment, Charles Townshend announced himself Pitt's successor."

"Champagne Charlie! The playboy of British politics!

That scoundrel changes his ideas as often as he changes his coat. He belongs to every party and cares for none. Uncle, Townshend will ruin America."

"I wouldn't go that far."

Patrick groaned. "I return to Williamsburg next week for a meeting of the legislature. That highflying kite, Townshend, without doubt, will give us trouble."

"Must you leave Sarah again so soon?" Uncle Patrick frowned. "I think your long absences encourage her moodiness and melancholy."

"The life of a woman whose husband is mixed up in colonial politics is far from easy. I hate to leave Sarah, but I feel it my duty to attend when the Burgesses meet. These are dangerous days, Uncle."

The Reverend Patrick Henry rose to leave. He grasped his nephew's hand. "My boy, I'm proud of your progress in this world. I remember when I taught you to recite:

> 'To learn and labor truly
> To get my own living.'

It seemed like a lost cause, but now you are a credit to our name. I apologize for ever saying I wished you bore another."

"Thank you, Uncle Patrick. Father still has his doubts about me, though. He thinks I'm a red-blooded radical."

"Perhaps you are," the Reverend Henry chuckled. "But that may be what we need to cope with people like Champagne Charlie."

On his arrival in Williamsburg, Patrick found a mysterious letter waiting for him. The fine copperplate handwriting on the heavy parchment looked impressive. Quickly, Pat broke the sealing wax and ripped open the paper. It was from Robert Carter Nicholas . . . of all people. Mr. Nicholas requested Mr. Henry's presence at his office on Francis Street, to talk about a matter of utmost importance. This letter was to be regarded as both urgent and secret. "Mention it to no one," Nicholas wrote.

Robert Carter Nicholas, the austere, conservative Treasurer of the colony, wanted to see him about a secret matter? Incredible! Ever since he joined the House of Burgesses, Nicholas had been politely cordial, but Patrick had not forgotten how he almost refused to sign his law license.

Curiosity consumed Pat. He lost no time getting to Francis Street. Robert Carter Nicholas received him with great solemnity. There were not many laughs in Treasurer Nicholas.

"Mr. Henry, ah-ah-ah- Patrick, pray be seated. You may perhaps wonder why I have sent for you."

That's a glorious understatement, thought Pat.

"When I was a student at William and Mary we often

quoted the amusing old proverb, 'A stitch in time saves nine.' "

Amusing as a dead cow, thought Patrick.

"You, I hope, will be my stitch in time."

I have been called a lot of things, but this is a new one.

"To be brief, I find my duties as Treasurer of the colony far too time-consuming. Before I collapse from overwork, I want you, Mr. Henry, to take over my law practice."

Patrick Henry almost fell off his ladderback chair.

"Mr. Nicholas, you can't mean *me!* Compared to a mountain like you, I am nothing but a molehill."

Robert Carter Nicholas actually smiled. "Twelve years have passed since I nearly refused to sign your license. I have watched you closely. I do not agree with your politics, but I do consider you one of the most able, hardworking young lawyers in Virginia."

Patrick was sure now that he was dreaming.

"In all honesty," Nicholas added, "I must tell you that I first offered my practice to young Thomas Jefferson."

"Oh." A little of the glow rubbed off the dream.

"He refused it. Mr. Jefferson is a student of the law. You, sir, are a lawyer. There is a vast difference."

Patrick jumped to his feet. "Mr. Nicholas, I am overcome. I accept your offer with pleasure. You do me the highest honor."

"Splendid. Now to more urgent matters. You've heard, I presume, of Charles Townshend's black deed?"

"No, I've been up in the country. But I am certain Champagne Charlie is bad luck for America."

"Precisely. Townshend announced in the House of Commons that the American colonies must be *forced* to yield to British authority. Thunderous applause encouraged his recklessness. He has now placed a tax on all glass, tea, paper, lead and paint that is shipped into America."

"All the things we get only from England!" cried Patrick. "Dastardly! Such taxation may fatten the English treasury — though not much — but it will lead to the loss of the American colonies."

"Not so loud, Mr. Henry. Your voice carries."

"Champagne Charlie will never hear the last of this!"

"I am afraid he already has."

"What do you mean?"

"Suddenly last September Charles Townshend dropped dead. But the Townshend duties are very much alive. What do you propose we should do about them, Mr. Henry?"

Patrick Henry set his square jaw and his blue eyes gleamed. *"We must combat them!"*

chapter 10

Wildcats and Rattlesnakes

THE explosion produced in America by the Townshend duties jolted the entire British Empire. Patrick Henry and his friends helped light the fuse.

To Henry, the Townshend duties were incredible. He consulted Richard Henry Lee, one of the liberal High-Blooded Colts in the House. "Look here, Rich, you were educated in England. Will you please explain the English to me? Didn't they learn anything from the Stamp Tax disaster?"

Lee, only four years older than Patrick, was far more sophisticated. The six distinguished Lee brothers grew up at Stratford, their family plantation in Westmoreland County, a gathering place for wealthy colonial leaders. The Lee brothers were wise in the ways of the world.

"My dear boy," said Richard Henry Lee, "at present the British do not care to learn. They are only interested in teaching. King George's latest Prime Minister, Lord North, says the Townshend duties will teach the Americans a valuable lesson."

"And how will the British enforce their miserable lesson?"

"Oh, they've put teeth into this tax, Henry. British inspectors can now enter and search any house in America."

"Enter a man's house and search it? Intolerable! The English make a mockery of freedom. Have they already forgotten their great lawyer Sir Edward Coke said 'A man's house is his castle'?"

"The British say the inspection is only to make sure everyone obeys the law."

"And if the naughty young colonies disobey the fat old parent who wants all the money? What then?"

"That's the worst of the whole rotten business, Patrick. They're going to ship all our so-called criminals to England for trial. You can guess what kind of justice a tax-fighting American will get in London. I'm afraid we're in for rather a nasty time."

"And to think Governor Botetourt was sent over here to glue up the rip between Virginia and England," said Patrick. "Then they stifle us with obnoxious taxes."

"Poor Botetourt," Lee shrugged. "I think he's secretly in sympathy with us, but a shortsighted devil like Lord North is too much for him."

All the colonies were in an uproar over the Townshend duties. The Tories defended the law by saying these were not *internal* taxes, such as the Stamp Act, that taxed American things. These were *external* taxes, applying only to goods shipped into the colonies. Such hairsplitting was laughable to the Young Colts.

In the House of Burgesses, Patrick Henry spoke more boldly than ever against the British. He attacked the Townshend duties as hard as he could.

"I say to you, gentlemen, that we must oppose the Townshend duties by which Parliament has degraded and enslaved us. The British believe half-witted Americans don't mind paying taxes . . . so long as they are not called taxes.

"Gentlemen, the Stamp Act was a tax. We opposed it. It was repealed. The Townshend duties are a tax. Oppose them with equal steadfastness, and *they* will be repealed.

"Are we such doltish people as to swallow the absurd distinction between *internal* taxes and *external* taxes? Is it disloyalty, is it sedition, is it treason to oppose the hand of tyranny? Never! We are free Englishmen, with the God-given right to tax ourselves, and we shall not yield that right to any power on earth — not to Townshend, not to Parliament, not to the King himself!"

A man sitting in the gallery — a Scotsman named Brad-fute — was so carried away he unconsciously spat tobacco juice onto the heads of the members, and almost fell over the railing. Some Tories said the tobacco stains were a fitting tribute to Patrick Henry's eloquence.

Patrick's smoldering words left no middle ground. On

one side stood Henry and the common man; on the other side, the aristocracy and the followers of the king. His daring speeches divided not only the House, but the entire population of Virginia.

"You realize what you've done, don't you?" said Tom Jefferson. "You've snatched the lead away from the men who have always guided the House, the Old Field Nags like Pendleton, Wythe, Bland, Randolph and the rest."

"Do you think we can carry them along with us tomorrow when we present our new resolutions?"

"Yes, but it'll be a struggle."

Jefferson's prediction was accurate. The struggle was vigorous, but the patriots won. After exhausting debate, the Old Field Nags agreed to send another protest to the king. Although these older men were cautious, they were attached to the main principle of freedom. In brief, the protest read:

DECLARATION OF PRINCIPLES

One — We declare that only the legislature of Virginia has the right to tax Virginians.

Two — We strongly protest the entering and searching of our homes.

Three — We also protest the trying of Virginians in law courts across the sea.

Four — We pledge our loyalty to the sacred person of
His Royal Highness, King George the Third.

Sacred person indeed, Patrick thought when the last
resolve was read. *The king is a headstrong lunatic and
they all know it.*

Word of the Burgesses' new resolutions reached Governor Botetourt as he was sitting down to dinner in the palace. He left his food untouched and hurried to the capitol.
Something had to be done at once.

About noon the Sergeant-at-Arms in the House of Burgesses called out: "Mr. Speaker, a message from the governor!"

The Burgesses became suddenly silent. The clerk of the
General Assembly strode down the aisle and halted. "Mr.
Speaker," he said, "the governor commands the immedi-
ate attendance of your House in his Council Chamber."

Speaker Peyton Randolph rose from his carved chair
and marched heavily out of the House. The Burgesses followed silently behind him, streaming up the stairs to the
Council Chamber. Every man was worried. What was up?
Governor Botetourt sat in his chair of state at the head of
the polished round table. His usual twinkle was gone. The
governor waited until the last members gathered round
the table and spread out along the walls. For a minute he
and the Burgesses looked squarely at each other. Then

Lord Botetourt said with angry dignity: "I have heard your resolves, gentlemen, and augur their ill effect. You have made it my duty to dissolve you, and you are, accordingly, dissolved."

The Burgesses turned and went back to their own House. They were boiling with indignation. Talking in low, excited tones, they got their hats and papers and walked out of the capitol. They kept right on walking until they reached the Raleigh Tavern.

"Mr. Hays," Peyton Randolph addressed the owner of the Raleigh in a strained voice, "Governor Botetourt has dissolved the House of Burgesses. We wish to continue our meeting here. Our presence may be dangerous to you."

"I am honored, sir," Anthony Hays said with a bow. "The Apollo is the largest room I have — it is at your disposal."

Filing into the Apollo Room with the others, Patrick glanced at the Latin motto carved above the mantel: *Jollity is the offspring of wisdom and good living.* Things did not look too jolly today. Pat recalled the first time Tom Jefferson had brought him to this beautiful room with its powder-blue paneling. That was nine years ago and everything was a good deal gayer then. So much had happened since. Tom's Fair Belinda, with whom he danced at the Apollo, was now married to another man

and Tom was paying court to a wealthy widow named
Martha Wayles.

Patrick himself had changed. Instead of soiled buckskin, he wore a velvet coat the color of peach blossoms
and a trim dark wig with two rolls curled over each ear
and a pigtail tied in back. Patrick's clothes were elegant
but his habits were plain. He was still a water drinker who
ate simple food, read the Bible every day, and never
swore, not even at the king.

As soon as the members of the House quieted down,
they elected Peyton Randolph moderator. It delighted
Patrick Henry to see the old guard taking the leadership
in this illegal, secret meeting.

Randolph called the meeting to order. Robert Carter
Nicholas took the floor. This conservative gentleman of
the law was indignant. "As you well know, gentlemen, I
believe we must, at all cost, maintain loyalty to Great
Britain. But the Townshend duties force even loyal Americans to take a bold stand." Governor Botetourt, by dis-
solving the legislature, had cemented together Burgesses
who, a short time ago, battled among themselves. "How,"
demanded Nicholas, "can we make our violent objections
felt?"

To everyone's surprise, the man who rose to answer
Nicholas was the man who never spoke in public: George
Washington. Colonel Washington had natural high color,

but now his cheeks were bright red with embarrassment.

"Ah — ah — ah —" Washington looked down at his feet and was silent. Patrick itched to help his inarticulate friend. "Speaker Randolph and members of the House, I am hesitant to address you, but I feel I have a message of value. Ah — ah — my friend and neighbor, Mr. George Mason, has drawn up a plan for a Virginia Association. He asked me to present it to you. Mason says if we join other colonies in a non-importation agreement we ah — ah — ah — ah, we can ah — ah be bothersome to the British." Washington sat down. He looked relieved.

Patrick Henry was quick to second the weakly worded suggestion. "Mr. Mason and Colonel Washington have given us a brilliant plan. We know American trade is vital to Great Britain. We have it in our power to bankrupt the British. Let us boycott their goods. Buy American! That is the only way to unrivet the chains and burst the bands of iron they fastened on us!"

"Pray, Mr. Henry, not so fast," said Robert Carter Nicholas. "How can we buy American when there is nothing American to buy? It seems to me we have the choice of buying from Great Britain or going naked."

"Improvise, sir, improvise!" Patrick answered hotly. "Let us wear homespun. Let us drink sassafras tea. Let us pound out our own pewter. Let us boycott the British!"

Washington's suggestion was unanimously adopted. The Non-Importation Agreement was drawn up and signed. Virginians would purchase no taxed article — tea, glass, lead, paint or paper. (An exception was made for very cheap paper. The colonists had to have that to do their work.) A long list of British goods was also forbidden. No more trading with England until the Townshend duties were repealed.

The Burgesses signed the agreements. Then they called slaves to bring glasses and wine. Ten toasts were proposed. One was to the king, and one was to the royal governor who had just dissolved the assembly. The old ties were still strong.

The Non-Importation Agreement spread swiftly from colony to colony. The Americans welcomed the plan. At last they had a sword to brandish against Parliament. Soon the colonies were gripped with a madness of manufacture and economy. Homespun became the proud badge of the patriot. The graduating classes at Harvard and William and Mary took their degrees in homespun. Virginians, planting vineyards and cultivating silkworms, dreamed of making their own wine and silk. The whir and rattle of loom and spinning wheel became the music of the American home.

Quite contentedly, Patrick hung up his peach-blossom velvet coat and put on homespun. He felt like himself once more. But the boycott met an odd resistance in the Henry household. Sarah refused to cooperate.

"I do not understand you, my dear," said Patrick. "George Washington himself says the home front is now in my lady's dressing room. You women are the chief consumers of British goods. To me, an American lady looks more attractive in a decent, plain dress made in this country than in the gaudy, butterfly dresses brought from Europe."

"I don't like these linsey-woolsey dresses," Sarah pouted. "They itch."

"Sarah! I'm astonished. Let me read to you from the Virginia *Gazette:*

TO THE LADIES OF VIRGINIA

Female patriots! One prudent matron, by strict economy within her family, will do more good for her country than 500 noisy Sons of Liberty, with all their mobs and riots. No more tea drinking and gossiping, Ladies of Virginia. Make your spinning wheels sing!

"Patrick Henry, don't read me another word of that nonsense. I won't have anything to do with your petty politics."

"*Petty?* Sarah dear, this is a matter of grave importance. America's freedom hangs in the balance."

"Let it hang."

"Sarah . . ." Patrick looked at his wife closely. Her large eyes had a strange gleam. She did not seem herself at all. "Sarah, why did you order a barrel of Wedgwood china from England against my orders?"

"English goods were ever the best." Sarah hung her head like a spoiled child.

"Today I canceled your order."

"You're a devil!" screamed Sarah. She ran out of the room, slamming the heavy door behind her. Patrick put his head in his hands. Some time later his oldest daughter Patsy found him still sitting in the same position.

"I quieted her down, Father. She's sleeping now."

"What's the matter, Patsy? I never knew your mother to act like this."

"Father," Patsy put her arm around his shoulder, "she gets upset easily these days. You're in Williamsburg so much you don't realize how she's changed. Sometimes Mother is hardly rational at all. Then the next day she's as sweet and dear as ever."

It did not occur to Patrick to call a doctor for his wife. In colonial times doctors were only for physical ailments and Sarah's physical health was excellent.

When Patrick Henry was worried, he got his dog and his gun and went hunting. This time he took Uncle Langloo along to cheer him up. They stalked through the woods all day, saying little. At night they sat by their

campfire under the stars and talked in hushed tones.

"That was delicious squirrel and rabbit stew, Langloo. You're a better cook than any I've met up with in Williamsburg."

"If you'd just bag a bear, Pat, I'd make you a real stew that Daniel Boone showed me. You take bear meat and chestnuts and sweet potatoes . . ." Langloo wiped gravy off his chin. "Wish you could see the way Boone uses old Tick-Licker — that's what he calls his long rifle. I learned a lot about cooking when him and me lived with the Cherokees. Did you know a Cherokee will eat any livin' critter, 'cept a man, of course. We even ate wildcat and rattlesnake. Tasty . . . but tough."

"I hear all Cherokees are tattooed, even the women. Is that right, Langloo?"

"Right as rain. They look like walking maps. Say, Pat, the Cherokees need your help. The whites wiped out their villages and wrecked their crops and pushed the poor old Cherokee back to land that don't even feed him. Can't you do something about them boundary wrangles, Pat?"

"I'm on the Indian Affairs Committee of the House, but we don't get much done. Too many people hate the Indians. I'd like to do something for the Cherokees, Langloo. I'll work on it when I return to Williamsburg." Patrick got up and tossed a log on the fire. Red sparks flew up into the darkness. "I dread leaving Sarah, Uncle Langloo. I'm worried about her."

"Why?"

"Yesterday she lashed out at me like a tigress."

"'Zat all?" Langloo cackled. "That's just the way

women act. Listen, Pat, I got good advice for you. Beware of a mule's hind foot, a dog's tooth, and a woman's tongue."

Patrick laughed. But he did not feel like laughing. His heart was gripped by a black fear. He knew something was seriously wrong with Sarah.

Patrick decided it was impossible to return to Williamsburg and leave Sarah. He persuaded her to go with him. "We'll take Dicy along to look after you when I'm busy at the capitol," he said. "You and Dicy can see the sights. But remember, no shopping. The boycott is going full tilt down there."

Patrick, Sarah and Dicy drove to Williamsburg in the Henrys' chaise. Caesar trotted along behind, his horse loaded down with bulging bags. As the carriage jolted over the bumpy road Sarah put her head on Patrick's shoulder. "I'm sorry I was bad about the boycott, Pat."

"Do you promise me to abide by it?"

"Promise. You have wonderful eyes, Pat." Sarah was clever at changing the subject. "Go outside on a cloudless day and look up at the sky and you'll see the exact color of your eyes."

"I only have eyes for you, Sarah," he chuckled. Patrick Henry was not a handsome man, except for his brilliant blue eyes. Large and deep-set, they were framed by long black lashes. His black eyebrows often knit together

in a straight line over his eyes, deepening their color to
dark blue. Whether serious or joking, Patrick Henry made
spirited use of his splendid eyes.

Usually, Patrick stayed at the simplest lodging in Williamsburg, but he recalled Tom Jefferson's remark, "People of quality prefer the Raleigh." Nothing was too good
for Sarah. Patrick persuaded Anthony Hays to put them
up in the Raleigh's finest room. The joys of Williamsburg
delighted Sarah. "I haven't been here since I visited my
Grandfather Parks when I was a little girl. I used to help
him print the Virginia *Gazette;* at least he said I helped.
But my gracious, Williamsburg has grown! Isn't it beautiful, Patrick? I never dreamed it would be so exciting."
Sarah seemed quite herself again.

As soon as she was settled, Patrick went to see his men-
tor, Robert Carter Nicholas. He found the Treasurer reading a packet of mail just in from London. Patrick heard
an unusual noise. It was Robert Carter Nicholas laughing.

"Listen to these cries of agony from the British, Patrick." Nicholas read in a loud voice. " 'The Americans
threaten our starving workers with clean teeth and empty
bellies. . . . New Englanders are tracking down import-
ers the way they used to hunt witches. . . . The wily
Virginians are trying to pull the wool over our eyes —
home-grown American wool.' We have them on the run,
my boy!"

"I hope so, sir. Mr. Nicholas, can we do anything to help the Cherokees?"

"How's that?" Nicholas put down his papers and looked over his glasses in amazement. "The Cherokees? Who wants to help those savages?"

"I do. I mean I promised a — a friend. They need help, sir. I looked up the record. The Treaty of Hard Labor forced them to yield to Virginia all their land east of the Great Kanawha."

"And what is so bad about that? Opening up western territory is important."

"Yes, sir. But there are twenty thousand people in the Cherokee nation. They lived on that land two or three centuries before white men set a foot on this continent. Those woods, streams, valleys and mountains are life's blood to the Cherokee. Many friendly Cherokees have been cruelly murdered along that border. Won't you speak to Governor Botetourt about them? He always listens to you, sir."

"All right, all right. Sometimes I think you're half Indian, Henry."

"I'd just as soon be. They're a great people, Mr. Nicholas. If only Americans understood them better!"

Patrick Henry never forgot Governor Botetourt's opening address at the new session of the House of Burgesses on November 7, 1769. Although the Burgesses were the same ones the governor had sent home in May, he said not a word about having dissolved them.

"Gentlemen," said Botetourt, "I am empowered officially to inform you that the Townshend duties have been repealed."

Repeal! Almost too good to be true, Patrick thought.

"I have been assured that His Majesty's government will lay no more taxes on America."

No more taxes? Patrick looked dubious. *That is too good to be true. I don't believe it.*

"It is my pleasure to announce that the boundary between our colony and the Cherokee nation has been reconsidered. Perhaps the new boundary will bring peace to that troubled territory."

Wait until the Cherokees hear this! They'll give Uncle Langloo a wildcat and rattlesnake banquet.

When Sarah complained crossly that she could not stand the wretched town of Williamsburg one more day, Patrick did not mind taking her back to Scotchtown. He had something he wanted to tell Langloo.

chapter 11

A Shock of Electricity

REPEAL of the Townshend duties brought a lull in the struggle between Virginia and the mother country. Distant rumblings could still be heard from the volcano that would soon blast smoke and fire.

Patrick Henry spent more and more time in court. He was a popular trial lawyer. His power over a jury was something wonderful. He played on the strengths and weakness of the jurymen the way a musician plays on a harp. As a criminal lawyer he had no equal.

A successful criminal lawyer in colonial times had to be resourceful. The poor devils who broke the law stood little chance of justice. Prison terms were almost unknown. A culprit might be branded on the hand and turned loose — or he might be taken to the gibbet and hanged.

Once Patrick defended a man named Rafe Morgan who unquestionably was guilty of murder. Like all good lawyers, Patrick was determined to free his client. In pleading the case Henry ignored Morgan and concentrated on the jury. Could God-fearing jurymen risk sending a man who *might* be innocent out to hang? Relent-

lessly he hammered on their consciences. Rafe Morgan
was found not guilty.

A member of the jury was asked to explain the surprising verdict. "Mr. Henry fixed us with those eyes of his
and told us if we voted for hanging we'd have to answer
for it on Judgment Day," said the juryman. "He scared me
out of my wits."

Patrick's services were in great demand. Sometimes he
was hampered by his lack of legal knowledge, but that
did not hurt his popularity. One day Patrick was in court
when a case was called for which he was not prepared. In
his haste Pat mistook the side he was on. He made a brilliant speech . . . for the wrong side.

When he sat down his distracted client cried, "I'm
ruined! You have undone me!"

"Give yourself no concern," Patrick said calmly. He
arose and once again addressed the judge and jury.
"Your honors, I have just stated what I presume is my opponent's side of the case. I shall now show you his reasoning is false, his claims groundless." Then Patrick utterly
demolished his own arguments and won the case. His
poor client was never the same again.

Patrick knew he needed to study more law. He asked
Tom Jefferson how to go about it. "Why don't you call on
Edmund Pendleton and get him to map out a course of
study for you?" Tom suggested.

"Pendleton? Why not your teacher George Wythe?"

"They're both brilliant lawyers. Pendleton is not as scholarly as Mr. Wythe and would be more on your level."

Sometimes I wonder if Tom Jefferson knows how his words bite, thought Patrick.

Patrick went to call on Edmund Pendleton and asked him for help. Pendleton, a good deal older than Patrick, stood at the top of the law profession. He was tall, graceful, strikingly handsome and beautifully educated.

"Why, Mr. Henry, I'd be delighted to assist you." Pendleton took a pinch of snuff from a silver box. "I understand you are somewhat aggressive and dramatic in court. I, myself, believe a good lawyer is at all times cautious and conservative."

Edmund Pendleton plotted a course of study for Patrick and even lent him the books to follow it through. But his praise of caution and conservatism was wasted. Patrick Henry was a born showman.

The very next day a poor old man named Zeke Tolliver asked Lawyer Henry to defend him against charges of hog-stealing. It did not occur to Patrick to turn the wretch away. Zeke reminded him of Uncle Langloo.

"Well, did you take the hog?" Patrick demanded.

"Yes, sir."

"Have you got the carcass?"

"Yes, sir."

"You go home, you scoundrel. Cut the pig in half length-wise. Hang as much of it in my smokehouse as there is in yours. That will be my fee for handling your miserable case."

In court Patrick Henry cast his piercing blue eyes on the judge and said almost reverently, "Your Honor, this poor man Zeke Tolliver has no more of that pig than I have. I'll kiss the Bible and take an oath on it."

The judge's verdict: not guilty. Patrick's methods might be questionable, but his clients usually won.

It was fortunate that Patrick practiced law success-fully because his daughter Patsy wanted to get married and he had to give her a dowry.

"But, Patsy," complained Patrick, who could not bear to part with his oldest child, "you're only nineteen. That's too young to marry."

"And how old were you, Papa, when you got married?"

"All right. I'll keep quiet, but it'll kill me to lose you."

Patsy was engaged to a distant cousin, young John Fontaine of Hanover, a member of a cultured French Protestant family.

"Will you perform the ceremony, Uncle Patrick?" asked Patrick Henry. "Here's a certificate for the two hundred pounds of tobacco which the law says we owe the parson."

"Thank you, my boy," said the Reverend Henry, taking the tobacco-money. "This is a nice coincidence. I was just thinking I would give Patsy two hundred pounds of tobacco as a wedding gift. It's yours, my dear girl, and God bless you."

All Virginia loved a lover and a marriage called for rejoicing and merrymaking. Patrick and Sarah Henry gave their daughter a gay wedding. Sarah rose to the occasion magnificently. To Patrick's surprise, she kept her unstable emotions under control and enjoyed all the festivities.

As the bridal party was returning to Scotchtown after the ceremony in Slash Church, the groom's friends spurred their horses to a full gallop and raced toward the house. The first one to reach Caesar, standing in the driveway, was handed a bottle of champagne decorated with white ribbons. The winner galloped back to meet the bridal carriage. The champagne was presented first to the bride and then to the groom. Each took a sip and passed it around the company. When it was Patrick Henry's turn he stood up in the carriage and said, "Here's to John Fontaine. May he ever be worthy of my daughter Patsy."

"Papa!" Patsy held a lace handkerchief to her face and blushed prettily.

John Fontaine answered his new father-in-law sol-

emnly. "Sir, I shall forever cherish your Patsy, not un-
mindful of the honor of fathering the first grandchildren
of Virginia's great leader, Mr. Patrick Henry of Hanover."

                    ❖   ❖

The period of quiet between England and America did
not last long, thanks to King George's clumsy new Prime
Minister. Lord North was a heavy stupid-looking man
who embarrassed his colleagues by taking catnaps in Parliament. He was destined to reduce the British empire to
the lowest point in its history.

Lord North wanted to tax the Americans just to make
them realize England still ruled the empire. The tax he
placed on tea was a disastrous step.

When news reached Virginia that Lord North had
broken the agreement not to tax America, Governor
Botetourt was deeply wounded. The idea of supporting
England's change of heart stunned him. Sick with disappointment, the governor took to his bed. He never got up
again.

The warmhearted Lord Botetourt had charmed the Virginians. They loved him and he returned their affection.
His illness, at a time when the colony needed friends in
high places, was a severe blow.

One day Lord Botetourt sent his messenger to the office

of Robert Carter Nicholas. Patrick Henry, who was doing some work in the office, let the messenger in.

"Mr. Nicholas, sir, the governor presents his compliments and requests your presence at the palace."

"Come along with me, Patrick," said Nicholas. "If you're to handle my affairs, you'd better learn your way around the palace."

Henry and Nicholas walked briskly across town. The cloudless October day was crisp and chilly. Sunlight seemed to dance in the crystal air. The catalpa trees bordering the Palace Green stood bare and black against an indigo sky. As they passed George Wythe's large brick house, Patrick gave a slight shiver. He might be able to consort with governors but he would never get used to Mr. Wythe.

Robert Carter Nicholas paused beside the iron-grilled palace gate. He pointed to the lion and unicorn, carved of stone and mounted on top of the brick pillars. "They are here, Patrick, to remind us we are British."

Patrick bit his tongue and said nothing.

The two visitors were escorted to the governor's bedchamber. Botetourt, dressed in ruffled nightshirt and cap, lay in a handsome walnut bed. Embroidered curtains hung from the carved canopy overhead. A fire blazed in the Delft-tiled fireplace but the governor appeared to be cold.

Feather quilts were piled on top of him. Patrick knew that Botetourt was only about fifty. He looked a hundred.

"My dear friend," said Robert Carter Nicholas. Tears filled his eyes. He could not go on.

Lord Botetourt looked at Patrick. "I see you brought the firebrand with you." The governor's eyes twinkled. "Good. We need him to warm things up. Rob, I want you to pray for me. I have spent so much time on women and wine and you're so wonderfully religious."

Nicholas smiled in spite of himself.

"Do you remember, Rob," the governor went on, "when I first arrived and you came to the palace to have a glass of Madeira with me? We sat in my charming parlor. Do you remember what you said?"

"I said 'Botetourt, you have here every good thing you could need or wish.'"

"Well, my dear Rob, I sent for you to let you see that I resign those good things with as much composure as I enjoyed them."

The governor closed his eyes. He seemed to be asleep. Then he opened his eyes and winked. The two men left quietly. They walked for some time in silence. Finally, Robert Carter Nicholas said, "Lord Botetourt's tact and friendliness helped us keep the peace. Without his help . . ."

A few days later Lord Botetourt died. Patrick Henry attended the services in Bruton Parish Church with Nicholas. It was the most elaborate funeral ever seen in Virginia. The governor's six cream-white horses pulled the black hearse to the William and Mary College chapel, where his lordship was buried.

The Virginia Assembly ordered a London sculptor named Richard Haywood to make a statue of Lord Botetourt dressed in his white wig and court robes. They placed the statue on the bar of the H-shaped capitol to keep his lordship's memory green. Engraved on the pedestal was a tribute beginning, "America, behold your friend —"

"It's a handsome statue of a charming fellow. I liked the governor a lot. We all did," Patrick said to Jefferson. "But, Tom, we can't just go on repeating 'we're all friends' while the British lower the tax boom and crack our skulls. I'd rather be friends with a rattlesnake than the present British government. At least a rattlesnake gives you a warning before he strikes."

"That's strong talk, Pat."

"This is the time for strong talk. You know as well as I do, Tom, the British slapped the blasted tea tax on us for one reason only — to keep alive their *right* to tax America."

"Well, they hit a tender spot. At least a million Americans drink tea every day. And because the British have an enormous surplus, they are selling their taxed tea for almost nothing."

Patrick Henry narrowed his eyes and rubbed his chin. "They think Americans will prefer cheap tea to liberty. They are mistaken. Instead of brewing tea, we are going to brew trouble."

Opposition to the tea tax spread like wildfire from colony to colony, uniting the Americans as nothing had before. Colonial doctors warned that tea drinking weakened stomachs and shortened lives. Housewives turned their backs on taxed tea and served miserable home-grown concoctions. The Sons of Liberty threatened British tea sellers with mob violence.

And then the powder keg exploded.

A messenger galloped into Williamsburg with breathtaking news. Boston patriots, dressed up like Mohawk Indians, had boarded English ships and pitched three hundred and forty-two chests of British tea into Boston harbor. John Hancock and Sam Adams were chief "pourers" at the Tea Party.

The outraged British were aghast at this "blow full in the face of the world." Conflict with the colonies had been, until now, a war of words; but Boston's wanton devastation of property galvanized the English into action. They ordered the port of Boston shut down. It did not matter

whether Boston survived or starved — she must be severely punished as an example to others. Benjamin Franklin wrote from London: "We never had so few friends in
Britain. The violent destruction of the tea seems to have
united all parties against us."

This was the dramatic moment Patrick Henry had been

waiting for. He called a meeting of the Hot Young Colts. They met secretly in an upstairs room at the Raleigh Tavern. Gathered around the pine table in the flickering candlelight were Patrick Henry, Tom Jefferson, Richard Henry Lee, his brother Francis Lightfoot Lee, and George Mason. They spoke in low, excited voices. Even the walls of the Raleigh might have ears.

"This time the British played right into our hands," said Patrick Henry. "They are *forcing* the colonies into united action."

"They don't think so," said Jefferson. "They are sure other colonies won't come to the aid of Boston and she will have to submit without a struggle. A copy of the *London Advertiser* arrived by today's packet. Listen to this: 'As soon as the British fleet heaves in sight off Boston, the Bostonians will scamper behind their counters, cast up their eyes to heaven and beg the king's forgiveness.'"

"The people of Boston," George Mason tugged on the lapels of his braid-trimmed velvet coat, "will turn their city into flames before they knuckle down to the British."

"We must help them. Boston is our front line in defense of American freedom." Richard Henry Lee let his orator's voice roll out the words. "If Boston's liberty is destroyed, British tyranny will sweep unchecked through —"

"For the love of heaven, Rich," said Francis Lightfoot Lee, who was twenty years older and somewhat steadier than his brother, "lower your voice or the Tories will sweep unchecked through the Raleigh and grab every one of us."

George Mason spoke quietly, pronouncing each word with emphasis. "I asked Colonel Washington his opinion. He said, 'The question is, should America sit spinelessly by and watch the British vultures devour one province after another?'"

No one spoke for a few minutes. These were violent words for a man who was as fair-minded as George Washington. Patrick Henry broke the silence.

"Gentlemen, we are of one mind. Boston needs help. Virginia must send it. But *how* can we arouse the people of Virginia? How can we get them to throw in their lot with strangers in far-away Massachusetts?"

Silence again. Henry had placed his finger on the heart of the problem. They had to communicate rebellious ideas to the masses, without being tried for treason.

"Little sympathy is wasted on Boston around here," said the older Lee, "and no amount of argument will move some people."

Tom Jefferson could contain himself no longer. "Have you thought of prayer, gentlemen?"

They all looked at Jefferson as if he had suddenly lost his mind.

"I don't mean here and now," he said quickly. His voice

was muffled with excitement. "I've been rummaging through my lawbooks and — well — I've cooked up a resolution. Resolved: that the people of Virginia set aside June first, the day the port of Boston is shut down — as a Day of Fasting, Humiliation and Prayer."

"Why that's brilliant!" exclaimed Patrick. "Can we get away with it?"

"There's precedent for it — good British precedent. It's right here in the records. Let me read —"

"Never mind," said Patrick hastily. "We'll take your word for it. What a splendid way to show our unity with Massachusetts! Even Tories who think Bostonians are sinners can't object to praying for them."

"And the governor could scarcely forbid our holding services in Bruton Parish Church," added Richard Henry Lee.

"Who'll we get to propose the resolution in the House?"

"How about you, Mr. Henry?" asked George Mason.

"Impossible. If I propose opening a window on a hot day, there are those who think my request reeks of treachery."

"It has to be a man who is dignified, impressive, religious, above reproach. A man respected by both sides." Jefferson's amber eyes gleamed in the candlelight. *"Robert Carter Nicholas!"*

"Perfect!" exclaimed Patrick Henry.

There was a sharp rap on the door. The men who huddled excitedly over the table leaned back with exaggerated casualness and began talking chitchat.

Anthony Hays, owner of the tavern, stuck his head into the room. "Excuse it, sirs. Just wanted to tell you Governor Dunmore's men have gone rolling home, full of ale and spy-talk. The coast is clear."

George Mason later wrote down his impressions of his visit to Williamsburg that historic spring. His reaction to Patrick Henry is interesting:

> Mr. Henry is by far the most powerful speaker I have ever heard. Every word he says commands the attention. Your passions are no longer your own when he addresses them. In my opinion he is the first man on this Continent in ability and public virtues.

Patrick Henry had agreed to ask Nicholas if he would present Jefferson's resolution. Patrick was prepared to use all his powers of persuasion; but it was like throwing his weight against an unlatched door. By now Mr. Treasurer was eager to strike a blow for freedom.

It was a beautiful May morning when Robert Carter Nicholas took the floor of the House of Burgesses. The many-paned windows stood open and outside birds sang in the glinting sunlight. Patrick Henry felt excitement rise within him. He looked at Tom Jefferson and smiled slightly. This was their day.

Nicholas read from the paper Tom had prepared.

> . . . being aware of the great dangers to British America from the hostile invasion of the city of Boston in our sister colony of Massachusetts, whose commerce and harbor are to be stopped by an armed force on the first day of June . . .

Patrick looked at the conservatives, Pendleton, Wythe, Randolph and the rest. They did not look shocked. Wythe was nodding his head in agreement.

> We move that the first day of June be set apart as a day of Fasting, Humiliation and Prayer to implore Almighty God to avert the evils of civil war which threaten us.

The resolution was unanimously adopted, each Burgess agreeing to alert his county. Within half an hour the Clerk of the General Assembly appeared with a familiar message: "Mr. Speaker, the governor commands the immediate attendance of your House in his Council Chamber."

Once again the Burgesses followed Speaker Randolph up the stairs to face the governor. The new governor was a coarse and brutal Scotsman, Lord Dunmore. He spoke curtly. "Mr. Speaker and Members of the House of Burgesses, I have in my hand a paper published by order of your House which reflects ill upon His Majesty and Parliament and makes it necessary for me to dissolve you. You are accordingly dissolved."

Once more the Burgesses flocked to the Raleigh Tavern and held an unlawful meeting in the Apollo Room. Again an association was formed to boycott British goods.

"It's the same thing over and over and over and over," muttered Patrick.

Richard Henry Lee thumped him on the back. "You're too impatient, Pat. We're progressing. At our next meeting I'm going to suggest we write to the other colonies and get them to send delegates to meet in a congress. We ought to coordinate our efforts."

"That's more like it," said Pat. "An attack on one colony *must* be considered an attack on all."

The patriots organized a committee to write to other colonies about what should be done. There was much secret writing back and forth. Patrick Henry and Thomas Jefferson helped forge this chain of words that linked colony to colony.

The night after the secret meeting at the Raleigh, the House of Burgesses was — of all things — the scene of a ball, and the guest of honor was — of all people — Lady Dunmore. It was an extraordinary evening. The members of the House bowed low to the wife of the man who had just dissolved them. It was an official occasion, but Patrick Henry chose to be absent. "Dancing with British ladies is not my dish of tea," he said. "And I mean tea with a tax on it."

Early on the morning of June 1, 1774, the bell of Bruton Parish Church clanged mournfully to proclaim the Day of Fasting, Humiliation and Prayer. The Burgesses assembled at the capitol and the Sergeant-at-Arms, bearing the silver mace, led them in stately procession down Duke of Gloucester Street. Silently they filed into the lovely old "court church" of colonial Virginia. The people of Williamsburg crowded in after them. Caesar climbed up to the balcony with the rest of the slaves. He was proud of his master's part in this awe-inspiring day.

The Burgesses settled themselves in the high-backed seats and fastened the door of each pew. Patrick looked at the royal governor's thronelike seat under the rich velvet canopy. It was empty.

The Reverend Mr. Price climbed the stairs of the lofty walnut pulpit and said in solemn tones, "Today a great seafaring city has been blockaded. Today a great seafaring people can look ahead only to empty wharves and ships rotting at anchor. The distance from Boston to Williamsburg is measured not only by the hazard of miles, but by the hazard of a common threat to our mutual welfare. Let us pray to Almighty God to give us one heart and one mind to oppose, by all proper means, *every* injury to American rights, and may God turn the hearts of the King and Parliament to wisdom and justice. Let us pray."

Throughout Virginia people knelt in prayer and left their food untouched. With some pride, Thomas Jefferson wrote in his diary: "The effect of the day through the whole colony was like a shock of electricity, arousing every man and placing him erect and solidly on his center."

Some of the tea tossed into Boston harbor had washed ashore in Virginia. At last the American colonies were beginning to draw together.

chapter 12

A Son of Thunder

PATRICK HENRY walked to the window of his mother's dark parlor to get a better light. The paper he was trying to read was covered with cramped writing. Rain pounded on the small windowpanes and Patrick felt it pounding on his heart, too. He was reading the last will and testament of Colonel John Henry. At the age of seventy-four, his father had suddenly died.

Colonel John Henry's will was not long. He had few worldly possessions to leave behind. All that he owned, he left to Patrick's mother. In the will he wrote out the directions for his funeral:

> I desire to be buried in a sober, decent manner, according to my quality. I request the burial service in the Book of Common Prayer, my brother, the Reverend Patrick Henry, to preach the funeral sermon. I wish to be buried in my uniform as a colonel of the King's militia. God save the King!

"God save the King," Patrick repeated. "He put that in for my benefit. He lived in America fifty years, but he was about as American as a bagpipe."

"They say Scotland's greatest export is men," said Uncle Langloo, who looked strange squeezed into an ill-fitting black suit. "He was a man, your father. A good man."

Patrick's mother, also in black, was seated in a rocking chair, weeping. She wiped her eyes and looked up. "Paddy boy, your father disagreed with your politics, but he was oh so proud of you. Don't ever forget it. I rejoice that he lived to see his youngest son become one of the leading men of Virginia."

"Shucks, sister," said Langloo, giving Mrs. Henry a love pat that almost knocked her off her chair. "Pat isn't one of the leaders; he's *the* leader. This boy could be elected king of Virginia tomorrow. Long Live King Patrick! Yippee!"

"Langloo Winston, will you kindly show proper respect for the dead? That's just exactly why Mr. Henry left careful directions for his funeral. He was afraid the Winstons wouldn't be proper. He never got used to our wild Winston ways, bless him. Patrick, tell me about Sarah. I'm sorry she couldn't come for the funeral."

"She's not well, Mother, not well at all. Someone has to be with her every minute. We never leave her alone now."

"Take care of her, son. She needs all your help."

Funerals in the eighteenth century were long and

elaborate. Sometimes there were sermons that lasted two hours. Uncle Patrick had the good sense to make his words short and to the point. "We mourn for our departed brother John Henry, colonel of the militia, justice of the peace, vestryman of the church, gentleman, scholar and man of character. Colonel John Henry left his mark on Virginia." The Reverend Patrick Henry paused. He cleared his throat. Then he said slowly, "A good life is the best sermon. Amen."

Riding back to Scotchtown after the funeral, Patrick kept repeating a phrase from the burial service, "Teach us to number our days, that we may apply our hearts unto wisdom." Wisdom was what he needed, infinite wisdom to deal with Sarah. He had not told his mother how bad things were. When he left home Sarah was locked in her room, screaming. She would not let him come near her. He hoped Dicy had been able to quiet her.

The rain was over and the sun had come out to set. A pale pink afterglow lit up the winter horizon. Two frosty white stars glittered in the rosy light. His wife's illness pressed down on Patrick like an iron weight. He looked up at the stars and said to himself, "From whence cometh my help? It cometh from the Lord."

Dicy ran out to meet him before he reached the house. "Oh, Mr. Patrick, I'm glad you're back. It's so awful! Miss Sarah, she fell down with a fever and she's bad off. Caesar got Dr. Dabney but he says there ain't nothing he can do. Miss Sarah, she's bad off."

Patrick ran up the stairs two at a time. He knelt beside Sarah's bed and called her name. She looked right at him but her eyes were blank. She did not know him. All night Patrick sat beside her bed. By morning he knew the worst. Her mind was gone.

Dr. Dabney told Patrick that Sarah's case was hopeless. He said they should take her to the new insane asylum in Williamsburg. Patrick would not hear of it. "My beloved wife will stay at Scotchtown," he said. "No matter how ill she becomes, we will care for her here."

First his father's death and now his wife's grave illness. It was too much. The slaves shook their heads and said, "The Devil's sittin' cross-legged. Everything's goin' wrong."

For the remaining five years of her life Sarah Shelton Henry was kept locked in one of the basement rooms at Scotchtown. Each day Patrick went downstairs to feed her, although she never recognized him. When he was away, Dicy and Caesar cared for her with untiring devotion.

Despite her sad fate, Sarah was better off than most mental patients in those days when mental illness was not understood — in fact it was considered a disgrace.

Bowed down under this crushing sorrow, Patrick returned to the political struggles in Williamsburg. Hard work eased his pain. Patrick and his friends wanted to form a union of the loosely connected colonies. John Randolph, the Tory leader, laughed at the idea. "What kind of a dish will a congress of the different colonies make?" he sneered. "New England will throw in fish and onions, the middle states flour and flax, Maryland and Virginia will add tobacco, North Carolina tar and turpentine, South Carolina rice and indigo. Georgia will sprinkle the whole mixture with sawdust. That is the kind of jumble you will get if you attempt a union between the thirteen British provinces."

Patrick Henry murmured that such a dish might be fit for a king . . . a pigheaded king.

At last all the colonies agreed to send delegates to Philadelphia for a Continental Congress. In Virginia a convention was held to select the seven delegates. To choose seven men from the colony's many brilliant leaders was a task. Gladstone, the famous British statesman, once said: "Colonial Virginia produced more great men than any other piece of real estate on earth, including Greece and Rome."

Thomas Jefferson did not attend the Virginia meeting. On the way to Williamsburg he was stricken with dysentery and had to return to Monticello, where his bride Martha nursed him back to health.

Jefferson, burning with zeal for freedom, hated to miss

that convention. He wrote a complicated letter explaining just why England had no authority over Virginia. He sent it to Patrick Henry and asked him to read it to the convention. Patrick did not do it, perhaps because the letter was too full of theories. Tom Jefferson was furious. He was touchy about his writing and he was proud of it. He thought his friend Pat had let him down. To Patrick's dismay, a crack appeared in their solid friendship. Jefferson never forgot the incident.

The minutes of that Virginia convention are lost but fortunately Edmund Berkeley of Middlesex County jotted down in his 1774 *Virginia Almanac* a tally of the voting. It gives us an idea of each man's place in the political sun.

Delegates		Votes
(1)	Peyton Randolph	104
(2)	R. H. Lee	100
(3)	Geo. Washington	98
(4)	P. Henry	89
(5)	Rich'd Bland	79
(6)	Ben. Harrison	66
(7)	Edm'd Pendleton	62
(8)	Thos. Nelson	51
(9)	Thos. Jefferson	51
(10)	G. Mason	16

For Patrick Henry to place fourth in this list of wealthy aristocrats was a feat. Peyton Randolph came first because he was the highly respected Speaker of the House of Burgesses. Next came Richard Henry Lee, who was responsible for calling the convention. Third was George Washington, Virginia's greatest leader of men . . . except when words were weapons. And then came the poorly educated young lawyer, Patrick Henry, the man of the people who spiced his speeches with the hot spirit of rebellion.

A fascinating picture of the Virginia delegation is found in a letter written by one of the voters, Roger Atkinson of Petersburg, Virginia. With a fine choice of words, he sketched several men:

Peyton Randolph

A venerable man, whom I well know and love — an honest man. Has knowledge, temper, experience, judgment — above all, integrity. A true Roman spirit.

Richard Henry Lee

I know the man and I like him. Need I say more? He was the second choice and he is my second choice.

George Washington

He is a soldier — a warrior. He is a modest man, sensible, speaks little. In action cool, like a Bishop at his prayers.

Patrick Henry

He is a real half Quaker, moderate and mild, and in religious matters a saint, but the very Devil in politics — a Son of Thunder.

Richard Bland

A wily experienced veteran at the bar and in the senate. Has something of the look of old musty parchments which he handles and studies much.

Benjamin Harrison

Brother-in-law to Speaker Peyton Randolph. I need not describe him.

Edmund Pendleton

The last and best, though all are good. The last shall be first says the Scripture. He is an humble and religious man, a smooth-tongued speaker.

George Washington invited Patrick Henry and Edmund Pendleton to stop at Mount Vernon on their way to Philadelphia. Patrick was delighted to get to see Colonel Washington's famous plantation. The great white house on the hill above the Potomac River was even handsomer than he had heard.

Martha Washington stood on the eight-columned porch waiting for the visitors. She greeted them with graciousness and warmth. She was short and plump and had beautiful brown eyes. "Ah, Mr. Henry, I have heard so much about you from my kinsman Captain Dandridge. How is he and how is little Dolly?"

"The Dandridges do splendidly, madam, but little Dolly is not so little any more. She's a beautiful young lady of eighteen who is being courted by a dashing redheaded Scot named John Paul Jones."

"And do you think she will marry him, Mr. Henry?"

"I rather hope not. Jones is a little too dashing for comfort."

At that moment Colonel Washington rode in from the fields, mounted on his favorite horse, Ajax. Patrick recalled Tom Jefferson's words: "Washington is the best horseman of the age — the most graceful figure that can be seen on horseback." Dressed in a plain blue coat, white vest, black breeches and boots, Washington did not look like the same man Patrick knew in Williamsburg. Not only his clothes, but his manner seemed different. He looked happy.

"My friends," exclaimed Washington, dismounting and handing Ajax to a waiting slave, "welcome to Mount Vernon. I am so pleased to have you here." Washington's smile was extraordinarily attractive.

The squire of Mount Vernon took his two guests on a tour of his twenty-five hundred acres. Patrick had never seen such an estate. There were five farms, orchards, a deer

park, a dairy, stables, kennels and even a large mill. George
Washington had been master of this plantation since he
was twenty, when he inherited it from
his brother. He knew and loved
every inch of it.

That evening George Ma-
son rode over for

dinner from his next-door plantation, Gunston Hall. Mason was a clear thinker with strong convictions. The three delegates were glad to have his advice before they left for Philadelphia. Over fine Madeira wine and oysters — Washington's favorite food — they talked of the events that lay ahead.

"I understand," said Mason, "that the Continental Congress will be made up of the wealthiest and most conservative men in America. Men who want peace at any price."

"I find no real connection between wealth and conservatism," said Patrick Henry. "Some of the bluest bloods in this colony are our strongest fighters against tyranny." He smiled tactfully at his three rich friends.

"Massachusetts is sending two hotheads," said Edmund Pendleton scornfully. "Sam Adams and his cousin John, both Harvard men. They are radicals."

"The Adamses are willing to risk all for freedom, if that's what you mean," said George Mason, who was trying to get a bill passed to free the slaves, and did not see eye to eye with the conservatives.

"Oh, those New England delegates will undoubtedly roar like bloodthirsty lions. We Virginians might have to restrain them. Cool heads must prevail." Edmund Pendleton, like most of the men going to Philadelphia, wanted to avoid everything that smacked of revolution.

"Above all," George Mason said, "you gentlemen must follow reason — wherever it leads you."

There was at Mount Vernon at least one person full of fire against the British and their ruthless policies. The next morning, peppery little Martha Washington talked to the three delegates, as Edmund Pendleton wrote later, "like a Spartan to his son before going into battle."

As the men mounted their horses and rode off, Martha stood in the doorway and waved. "God be with you, gentlemen!" Then she called out, "I hope you will stand firm against the British. I know George will."

Fifty-two delegates from twelve colonies assembled in Philadelphia for the Continental Congress. Only the colony of Georgia was absent. The gentlemen, dressed in knee breeches, full-skirted coats, ruffled shirts, and three-cornered hats, met at New Tavern and marched in a body to the handsome new brick building called Carpenters' Hall. Philadelphians stopped to stare at the distinguished strangers. Some even saluted and cheered. Patrick felt as though he were marching to battle.

The congress convened in the East Room of the hall, a cheerful room with buff-colored walls, white woodwork and a low, white-paneled fireplace. Morning sunlight streamed through the high windows. The delegates could look out and see the masts of sloops and schooners anchored off Dock Street. Most of the ships had brought goods from England. The colonies were not allowed to trade elsewhere.

The congress got off to a slow start. The roll was called and officers elected. To the delight of the Virginia delegation, Peyton Randolph was chosen president. Then the room was silent. The situation was tense. As John Adams wrote his wife Abigail, "The fifty gentlemen, all strangers, not acquainted with each other's language, ideas, views, designs, were jealous of each other — fearful, timid, skittish." Each delegate feared to speak lest he tread on someone else's toes.

At last one man suggested a prayer. John Jay of New York said, "No one can expect Baptists, Presbyterians, Congregationalists, Episcopalians, Quakers, Catholics and Jews to unite in worship."

Sam Adams, the untidy rebel from Massachusetts with a price on his head, said, "I can listen to a prayer from a gentleman of piety who is a patriot. Let the Reverend Mr. Duché lead us in devotions." This was typical of Sam Adams's genius. The Reverend Duché was an Episcopalian. The Southern delegates, mostly Episcopalians, were suspicious of the Congregationalists from New England. At one stroke, Adams quieted their fears.

The minister read from the Thirty-fifth Psalm. The words surprised his listeners. "Plead thou my cause, oh

Lord, with them that strive with me, and fight thou against them that fight against me."

After the prayer a deep silence settled on the assembly. No one seemed willing to start. Who could predict what dangers lay ahead? The stillness became unbearable, yet no one broke it.

Then the tall figure rose hesitantly to his feet. Everyone turned to look at him. He was dressed in a plain suit of parson's gray. His brown wig was unstylish; his shirt had no frills. At first, words came slowly. After apologizing for his inability to do justice to the subject, he began to list the wrongs done to the colonies. As he gathered momentum, he spoke clearly and forcefully. One delegate reported, "even those who had heard Patrick Henry in all his glory in the House of Burgesses were astonished at the way his talents seemed to swell to fill the larger stage on which he was now placed."

His words were edged with danger. "Government is at an end. Where are now your landmarks, your boundaries? All distinctions are thrown down. All America is thrown into one mass. The distinctions between Virginians, Pennsylvanians, New Yorkers and New Englanders are no more. *I am not a Virginian, but an American!*"

The men of the Continental Congress were stunned, almost hypnotized. Even those who violently disagreed admired the man's daring and eloquence. *An American —*

what in the name of heaven was that? Henry's words were
crazy. Obviously, government was not dissolved. Obviously, rigid boundaries divided each colony. Yet in this man
there was a fervor that was contagious. John and Sam
Adams, eager to enlist other colonies in the defense of em-
battled Massachusetts, could not conceal their delight. The
Virginia delegates, even glacial Edmund Pendleton,
glowed with pride in their native son.

From that day, the best-known orator in Virginia became the best-known orator in America. They called him
a Son of Thunder. And while Patrick Henry thundered,
storm clouds blackened.

chapter 13

The Voice of the Revolution

Scotchtown
Hanover, Virginia
October 15th, 1774

Dear Madam:

I thank you for your kind hospitality.

My son Patrick has gone to Philadelphia near seven weeks. The affairs are kept with great secrecy, nobody being allowed to be present. I assure you we have our lowland troubles with respect to Great Britain.

Here people have been very sickly but hope the sickly season is nigh over. My son's wife continues to be extremely ill.

I am, dear madam, your humble servant,

Sarah Winston Henry

This is the only letter in existence written by the mother of Patrick Henry. It was addressed to Mrs. William Fleming, a friend Sarah Henry had been visiting. The letter is remarkable because in those days few women were that well educated.

Mrs. Henry had no way of knowing that the men of the Continental Congress were agog over her son's *I am an American* speech. John Adams and his cousin Sam talked it over in their room in Miss Jane Port's lodging on Front Street.

"I thought Mr. Henry was splendid. I took notes," said John Adams, who always wrote down everything. "They're right here in my pocket. The man's voice is like organ music. It goes through to the bone."

"Fine speech." Sam shrugged his heavy shoulders. "Too strong for Congress to swallow, of course, but a good stimulant. The reception committee that came to greet me was typical." Sam Adams raised his voice to a squeaky soprano. " 'Please, Mr. Adams, whatever you do, don't *mention* the idea of independence.' " Sam shook his head. He looked like a shaggy lion. "People avoid me like a man infected with leprosy because I believe we should break away from Great Britain."

"Don't rush things, Sam. It all takes time. Right now people think we can come to terms with the British. But they'll find out. Are you coming with me to Dr. Cadwalader's dinner for the delegates?"

"Another sinful feast? Never. Curds, creams, jellies, sweetmeats, tarts, trifles, floating islands, whipped silla-bubs, and bowls of lemon punch big enough for geese to swim in! I'm sick of it all. If food were a weapon, the people of Philadelphia could bury the Continental Congress in a common grave."

That night John Adams wrote his wife Abby: "Sam eats little, drinks little, sleeps little, but thinks much. The claret-colored coat his friends bought for him when he left Boston has spots on it and the pleats are as wrinkled as if congress had sat for a year, but Sam is unaware. He has more important things to think about, such as breaking up the British Empire."

The Continental Congress surrounded its meetings with the strictest secrecy. The delegates feared the anger of the British. The secretary, Charles Thomson, guarded the minutes of the meetings with his life; yet the British government was kept informed of all that went on. Obviously, spies lurked in the congress. The Tory newssheet *Royalist* warned the American delegates: "Your necks may be inconveniently lengthened, if you don't look out." Delegates who read that felt a chill.

Members of the congress were arguing over a letter of protest to King George when a flurry of excitement almost broke up the meeting. A rider galloped up to Carpenters' Hall, jumped from his horse and strode breathlessly into the East Room. It was Paul Revere, silversmith, dentist, cartoonist, coppersmith, soldier, express rider, and lover of liberty.

"Bad news from Boston! General Gage is mounting

cannon on Beacon Hill, digging trenches, throwing up breastworks! It looks as if the British are getting ready to fight."

War! It was out of the question — unthinkable. Alarmed and outraged, the delegates broke into excited chatter.

Paul Revere brought with him strong resolutions drawn up by Dr. Joseph Warren and passed by the inflamed citizens of Boston. The Bostonians referred to the British in violent words ("The streets of Boston are thronged with military executioners"). They resolved that every town and district would form a strong militia and that taxes should be paid to local governments, not to Great Britain. Revere asked the congress to support the Massachusetts colony.

Patrick Henry was fascinated. He pushed his glasses up on his forehead and looked around. Could this conservative congress approve such resolutions? Joseph Galloway of Pennsylvania announced, "For congress to back these resolutions is practically a declaration of war."

George Washington wanted action. "I will raise a thousand men at my own expense," he stated, "and march myself at their head for the relief of Boston."

As the argument went on, Patrick watched the men from Massachusetts. They sat bolt upright, not daring to look to the right or left. So much depended on getting help; Massachusetts could not go it alone. At last the vote was taken. The resolutions passed. The Massachusetts men jumped up and shook hands with everybody.

That night John Adams wrote in his diary: "One of the happiest days of my life. This day convinced me that America will support Massachusetts or perish with her."

Before leaving Philadelphia the delegates gathered at

Daniel Smith's City Tavern for a farewell party. Patrick Henry sought out John Adams. During the seven weeks in Philadelphia a firm friendship had sprung up between them. Adams wrote to his wife (how thankful we are to John Adams for his diary and letters), "Not one member except Patrick Henry appeared aware of the precipice or rather pinnacle on which we stood and had courage enough to acknowledge it."

"Well, Mr. Adams," said Patrick, "it's all over. How do you think our appeals will be received in England?" Patrick already knew the answer. He just wanted to hear Adams say it.

"Mr. Henry, when all our statements of rights, listings of wrongs, resolutions, petitions and appeals to the king reach London," Adams paused dramatically, "they will be used as wastepaper."

Patrick flashed his wonderful smile. "You sound about as hopeful as your cousin. I think Sam Adams is one of the most interesting men at this convention."

"Sam is an original, all right. He's the only man I know who is absolutely indifferent to money or power. Sam is an example of the old saying that there's no limit to what a man can do when he doesn't care who gets the credit. But Mr. Henry, who do you think is the greatest man in our congress?"

"I believe the man who has more solid judgment and information than anyone present is Colonel George Washington."

"Washington is dedicated to the cause of freedom," John Adams agreed. "But only you and I and Sam and Mr. Gadsen of South Carolina are ready to declare independence. And, Mr. Henry, I believe that after all, we must fight for just that."

Patrick looked at the plump, short man with the high forehead and heavy eyebrows, whom the Tories called John the Roundhead. "By God, Mr. Adams," he replied, "I am of that mind." These words burned themselves into John Adams's memory because he knew Patrick Henry was a deeply religious man who never took the Lord's name in vain.

Benjamin Harrison and Richard Henry Lee approached the two radicals; they were sipping burgundy and gloating over the success of the convention. "I would have gone to this meeting if it had been held in Jericho," said the luxurious-looking Harrison, who was handsomely dressed in smooth blue broadcloth. "I'm confident we have averted war."

"Alas, I do not share your confidence, sir," said John Adams.

The two men looked at each other with irritation. Unknowingly, they had a large stake in America's future. John Adams was to be President of the United States and his son, John Quincy Adams, likewise. Harrison's grandson, William Henry Harrison, and his great-grandson, Benjamin Harrison, would also become Presidents.

"We will carry all our points," Richard Henry Lee said enthusiastically. "All the hated acts will be repealed. The army and the fleet will be recalled and Britain will give up her foolish project."

Adams and Henry exchanged glances but said nothing.

Benjamin Harrison turned to Patrick. "You, Mr. Henry, keep talking as though you think Great Britain will drive her colonies to extreme action."

Patrick Henry let Benjamin Harrison have the full force of his blazing blue eyes. "Sir, she *will* drive us to extremities. Hostilities will *soon* commence and a desperate and bloody fight it will be."

Benjamin Harrison and Richard Henry Lee looked shocked. Even for a liberal like Lee, this kind of talk was too strong. They bowed politely and departed. As they left, Patrick heard Harrison say, "It sounds to me as if young Henry *wants* a war."

Patrick looked at John Adams in dismay. Adams patted him on the back. "That's the way people always talk when they get a dose of the unvarnished truth."

The farewell party ended with a toast proposed by the President of the Congress, Peyton Randolph. Lifting his glass he said solemnly, "May the sword of the parent never be stained with the blood of her children."

John Adams muttered to Patrick, "That's not a toast. It's a prayer. Let us join in."

As soon as Patrick returned to Hanover he called a meeting of the militia at Merry Oaks Tavern. He told the men in plain words to prepare for any emergency. "If worse comes to worst, we must combat the British with musket and cannon."

Some of the older militiamen shook their heads and said "Colonel John Henry must be turning in his grave." But the younger men responded to Patrick's leadership. The Independent Company of Hanover got ready for battle.

Reaction in England to the Continental Congress was strong, either pro or con. William Pitt (now Lord Chatham), recovered from his mental breakdown but still physically ill, rose in the House of Lords and demanded the removal from Boston of the British troops. "I must declare that in all my reading of history," Pitt said, "for wisdom under difficult circumstances, no body of men has surpassed the congress at Philadelphia. I trust it is obvious that all attempts to impose servitude on such men must be fatal."

It was not obvious.

The pompous thirty-seven-year-old king, George III,

announced: "I wish nothing but good. Therefore, every-one who does not agree with me is a traitor and a scoun-drel." He told Lord North, "The die is cast. The colonies *must submit.*" Lord North knew what was good for him. He agreed with the king.

Great events generate great leaders. Not once did Pat-rick Henry waver or doubt his course, and he drew the people of Virginia right along with him. George Wash-ington stood ready to serve his country, but he never spoke in public. Thomas Jefferson, whose brilliant mind was so important in the struggle with England, was a pen-and-ink man. At this fork in history, it was Patrick Henry, the Voice of the Revolution, who blazed the trail.

The brilliant summit of Patrick Henry's Revolutionary leadership was reached on March 23, 1775, when he was almost thirty-nine years old. The scene was St. John's Epis-copal Church on a hilltop in Richmond. The occasion was the Second Virginia Convention. The meeting had to be held in Richmond because Governor Dunmore would not allow it in Williamsburg. St. John's was chosen because it was the largest building in Richmond.

Yellow daffodils and golden forsythia were blooming in the churchyard that spring morning and a soft breeze blew through the open windows. One hundred and twenty dele-gates crowded into the high-backed pews. The cream of Virginia was assembled — George Washington, Thomas

Jefferson, Peyton Randolph, Robert Carter Nicholas, Benjamin Harrison, Richard Henry Lee — all the leaders were there.

The meeting was called because the British government had indeed paid no attention to the petitions sent by the Continental Congress. King George sent an iron answer — a saber-rattling army and a fleet of warships. He directed General Gage to punish colonists if they did not obey.

The question before the convention was: What should be done next?

Patrick Henry wanted Virginia put on a military alert, ready to fight, as his company in Hanover was. Thomas Jefferson and Richard Henry Lee supported him, but most men at the convention objected. Edmund Pendleton said it was every man's duty to obey the king. Robert Carter Nicholas said the king would never permit British subjects to fight one another. Yet even the Tories knew time was short. "War may come," they admitted, "unless certain things are done."

Patrick Henry, a man of divine impatience, swept away every "if" and "unless." "Why talk of things being now done to avert war?" he cried. "*It is too late.*"

Argument grew more heated. The friction kindled a flame within Patrick, but like the ancient Greeks he banked his fires. One of his secrets as a speaker was he never lost his temper, even when debate was at its hottest. He was always in control of the situation. At last he could contain himself no longer. He rose to speak.

In the library of Cornell University there is a manuscript containing a description of Patrick Henry's greatest speech by John Roane, who was present at this historic event. "Henry began calmly," Roane says, "but smothered excitement soon showed in his face and voice."

"This is no time for ceremony," Patrick said in a voice of cold steel. "British bayonets will soon control the country. It is a question of freedom or slavery!"

Shivers went up and down the spines of the delegates. Each man thought Patrick was looking him straight in the eye.

"For my part, I am willing to know the whole truth; to know the worst, and to provide for it." A delegate got up, his hand raised. But Patrick did not pause. "We have done everything that could be done to avert the storm that is now coming on. There is no longer any room for hope. If we wish to be free . . . we must fight! I repeat it, sir, *we must fight.* An appeal to arms, and to the God of Hosts, is all that is left us!"

In great oratory the appearance of the speaker always changes. Patrick Henry seemed to grow taller and there was about him an electric excitement generated by his vibrant voice and flashing eyes.

"They tell us, sir, that we are weak, unable to cope with an enemy so powerful. But when shall we be stronger? Will it be the next week, or the next year? Will it be when we are totally disarmed and a British guard shall be stationed in every house?

"Sir, we are not weak, if we make proper use of those means which the God of nature placed in our power. Three millions of people armed in the holy cause of liberty, and in such a country as we possess, are invincible.

"The battle, sir, is not to the strong alone. It is to the vigilant, the active, the brave. It is now too late to retire from the contest. There is no retreat but in submission and slavery. Our chains are forged. Their clanking may be heard on the plains of Boston. The war is inevitable. And let it come! I repeat it, sir, let it come!"

According to John Roane, the tendons of Henry's neck stood out like whipcords. His voice rose louder and louder until the walls of the church seemed to shake in the vibrations.

"Gentlemen may cry peace, peace, but there is no peace. Our brethren are already in the field. Why stand we here idle? What is it that gentlemen wish? What would they have? Is life so dear, or peace so sweet, as to be purchased at the price of chains and slavery?"

Patrick bowed his head and crossed his wrists. Chains were almost visible upon his arms as he stood there a prisoner in agony. After a solemn pause, he raised his eyes and chained hands toward heaven and prayed in tones that thrilled every ear:

"Forbid it, Almighty God!"

Then he turned to the Loyalists, who were quaking at the thought of taking part in treason against the king. He slowly bent toward earth, his hands still crossed. He seemed weighed down with chains, a slave without hope.

"I know not what course others may take . . ."

Suddenly he rose and exclaimed:

"But as for me . . ."

He spoke the words through clenched teeth. His body was thrown back, every muscle strained. The pale face and glaring eye became terrible to look upon. Men leaned forward in their seats, their faces pale and their eyes glaring.

Then came the loud, clear, triumphant notes:

"Give me liberty . . ."

And as each syllable of *liberty* echoed through the room, the links of his chains were shattered. He opened his hands and raised his arms. His face was radiant. He stood erect and defiant — a free man.

A pause. Then he let his left hand fall powerless to his side and clenched his right, as if holding a dagger with the point aimed at his breast. In awful cadence he intoned:

"Or give me death!"

With a blow he seemed to drive the dagger into his heart.

Outside the church, Colonel Edward Carrington, com-

pletely carried away, jumped from the windowsill, where
he was listening, and stamped the ground, crying, "When
I die, bury me here, on this spot!" (Years later, he was
buried there.)

Inside the church, there was a nerve-tingling silence. No
word was spoken; no applause heard. And if ever a silence
was eloquent, that one was. For in that silence the swift
currents of history were swirling. As happens perhaps once
in a generation, the right, strong words, marvelously spoken by one leader, had determined the course of the future.

chapter 14

P. Henry, Outlaw

PEYTON RANDOLPH and Richard Henry Lee, the two elegant, intelligent aristocrats, sat beside the pine-paneled fireplace in the corner of the taproom at the Raleigh Tavern. Smoking their clay pipes and sipping ale from pewter mugs, they discussed only one subject — Patrick Henry's speech in St. John's Church.

"It was the greatest speech I ever heard," said Lee — himself a noted orator. "By the time he cried *Give me liberty, or give me death,* I felt sick with excitement. What an experience! People expect to hear great oratory at a banquet or in a church or in a lecture hall. But a great speech is given only once. The time is ripe. Mighty issues hang in the balance. The moment arrives — and the man speaks."

"That's the way it was," said Peyton Randolph. "Henry's passion melted us into one mass. As soon as the convention voted to arm Virginia, it was clear his words were not just words, but action."

"Some people," Lee lit his long pipe and leaned back in his chair, "are afraid of great speakers. They say oratory is a black art that often misleads men. Why not a simple statement of truth instead? Well, unfortunately, many of us need persuasion to *see* the truth."

Peyton Randolph patted his generous stomach with widespread hands. " 'There went a smoke out of his presence and a consuming fire out of his mouth.' That's from the Old Testament, Mr. Lee, but it might have been written about our friend from Hanover. None of us who were in St. John's that day will ever forget what we saw and heard."

The eighteenth century was a time of great oratory. At almost the same moment that Patrick Henry was overwhelming the Virginia convention, Edmund Burke was making a brilliant speech in the House of Commons. He called upon the British for one last desperate effort to pacify the American colonies. "The stronger power may offer peace with honor and safety," Burke said. But no one listened.

Burke's excellent plan was rejected. Instead, Lord North sent an order to his generals: *Crush the spirit of liberty among the Americans.* General Gage replied he needed only four regiments to do the job. Apparently he agreed with General Wolfe that "The Americans are the dirtiest, most contemptible, cowardly dogs imaginable."

With war clouds massing in the distance, Patrick Henry dreaded the stormy days ahead. Weary and lonely, he returned to Scotchtown for a short rest. Even though Sarah was hopelessly ill, it comforted him to be near her; and the companionship of their children meant a great deal to him. Unlike most stern colonial parents, Patrick was close to his children. He romped with them in a rowdy way that would have shocked his fellow Burgesses.

Patrick and twelve-year-old Willie got up before breakfast and went horseback riding. "Race you!" yelled Willie, and off they went across the fields at a dead gallop. Mounted on the swift Shandy, Patrick won every race. He played hard; "letting" children win was out of the question.

Father and son walked their horses home through the woods to cool them off. Steam rose from the horses' flanks and sweat streaked their coats. The woods, alive with the first faint green of springtime, were laced with white dogwood.

"Papa," said Willie, "something's bothering me."

"What, son?"

"Everywhere I go people repeat your motto, 'Give me liberty, or give me death.'"

"Yes?"

"It sounded wonderful . . . until I heard Caesar say it."

"Ouch."

"If you're that strong for liberty, Papa, how come we have slaves?"

Thoughtfully, Patrick patted Shandy on his damp withers. For a long time he was silent. A blue jay flashed by cawing "Thief! Thief! Thief!"

"To tell you the absolute truth, son, we could not run this plantation without slaves."

"But is slavery wrong?"

"By all that's holy, it is wrong. I will not, I cannot, justify it."

"Why does Virginia keep bringing in new slaves? This week at Petersburg they're auctioning two hundred more."

"The Burgesses want to stop it, Willie, but the English won't listen. Trading African slaves for American tobacco, sugar and indigo is the lifeblood of the British Empire."

"The British must think slavery is all right."

"Willie, any thinking person, anyone who takes the Bible seriously, *has* to loathe slavery. No real man could want to see his country the gloomy retreat of slaves."

"Then why don't you give our slaves liberty, Papa?"

"Where would they go? What would they do? Someday, Willie, this atrocity will come to an end, but no man, or even group of men, can stop it now. Until that day, son, we must be kind to the slaves — we must hate slavery — and we must pray to God to deliver us from this evil."

While Patrick was refreshing himself at Scotchtown, Williamsburg burst into an uproar. It was the kind of violent excitement a man like Patrick Henry would hate to miss.

To cripple the colonies, the British decided to seize American war supplies. In Massachusetts, General Gage sent troops to destroy the arms and ammunition at Concord. The six hundred red-coated British soldiers were met at Lexington by seventy Minute Men.

"Don't fire unless fired on," shouted the Yankee leader Captain Jonas Parker. "But if they want a war, let it begin here!"

And right there the bloody struggle began.

The very next day — April 20, 1775 — Governor Dunmore tried to seize the war supplies in Williamsburg. Dunmore, a coarse oaf with "no manners, no religion, and no intelligence," disliked and feared the Virginians. He had long kept an eye on the eight-sided powder magazine with the cone-shaped roof. The ammunition in there was supposed to be used in case of Indian attack, but you never could tell what these crazy Americans would do. Now Dunmore sent an order to the Royal Marines: "Get that powder."

In the dead of night, Captain Harry Collins and a detachment of British marines left the armed schooner *Magdalen*, anchored in the James River, and sneaked ashore. With great stealth they crept into Williamsburg and broke into the powder magazine. Working silently and swiftly, they loaded fifteen barrels of gunpowder into Lord Dun-more's wagon. They tossed a cover over it and drove off into the darkness. The clatter of wooden wheels over the cobblestones woke the people of Williamsburg. Cries rang through the night.

"It came from the magazine!"

"They're stealing the powder!"

"To arms! To arms!"

Drums rolled, dogs barked, people yelled. Lanterns and torches swayed and bobbed through the dark streets. Angry citizens rallied around the powder horn. But there was nothing they could do. The British were gone . . . and so was their powder.

News of the "Rape of the Gunpowder" flew through the colony. Inflamed patriots grabbed their guns, jumped into the saddle and headed toward Williamsburg. This called for action.

It was Uncle Langloo who galloped up to Scotchtown to bring the news to Patrick. Just as Sam Adams cheered over the British attack on Lexington and Concord, Patrick Henry gloated over the theft of the gunpowder.

"This is it, Langloo," said Patrick, rubbing his hands together. "Dunmore's rashness will set off an explosion of anger. By forcing the people into action, he's given the American cause a great boost. We can talk from now to doomsday about taxation and representation. The people

shrug and say it's not their worry. But rob them of their gunpowder, and they'll dash to defend themselves."

"I heerd old Peyton Randolph talked some of the boys into turning back. He sent out a letter saying everything would be linsey-woolsey and for the patriots to go on home."

"*Go home?* How could Peyton Randolph *be* so stupid? If we hand Dunmore an easy victory, we're finished. I've got to do something about this, and quick."

"Now you're talking, Paddy boy. Yippee! Let's go!" The old man slapped his leather breeches and danced a little jig.

"Hold on, Uncle Langloo, maybe you're too . . ." Patrick shook his head. "Oh, the devil take it. You have more fire than men half your age. Come on, we've got work to do."

"Leave it to us Winstons," crowed Langloo. "We'll round up everybody. We'll even raise up the dead and set 'em marching on Williamsburg. Only not your Pa, Pat. We'll leave the Loyalists lay."

Patrick Henry, "assisted" by Langloo, sounded a call to arms. He sent express riders around the county with the message: *Meet me at New Castle on the second of May on business of the highest importance to American liberty.*

The men of Hanover and their neighbors rallied round with spirit. They assembled at the village of New Castle on the Paumunkey River. Patrick Henry climbed on a stump and made one of his rousing speeches. Fired by the prospect of action, his eloquence was wonderful. "Seize Dunmore by the throat!" he cried. "Now, if ever, we must strike for freedom!"

"Hooray for Captain Henry!" the men cheered.

"The Devil with Dunmore!"

"On to Williamsburg!"

"Pay for the powder or fight for it!"

The march on Williamsburg began, Captain Patrick Henry leading the way. His aide-de-camp, "Corporal" Langloo Winston, clanked along behind him. Patrick's blood pounded with excitement. After ten years of words, words, words, at last he had a chance to act against British tyranny.

Tories along the line of march ran out to beg Captain Henry not to plunge Virginia into war. He forged on, relentless. The Hanover Volunteers marched behind him singing and counting in cadence. Patriots along the way joined the ranks. Soon close to five thousand men marched in Henry's "army."

About sunset Captain Henry called a halt. He and his men camped for the night near Doncastle's Ordinary, an inn sixteen miles from Williamsburg.

News that an army was marching on the capital terrified Governor Dunmore. "Pay for the gunpowder or fight for it?" he repeated. "They may attack at daybreak? Oh, this is a disaster!"

Dunmore acted swiftly. He hurried his wife and family aboard the British man-of-war. He called out the marines. He ordered cannon placed on the Palace Green. But it was Patrick Henry's name that worked magic. When Dunmore heard the hated Henry was leading the oncoming horde, his resistance collapsed. He sent a messenger galloping out to meet them.

Patrick spotted the cloud of dust down the road. He halted his troops and waited. The messenger pulled up and saluted. "Captain Henry, sir, a message from Governor Dunmore. He sends you this three hundred and thirty pounds in payment for the gunpowder he removed from the magazine for reasons of public safety."

"Public safety. Ha!" muttered Langloo. "Private stoopidity."

The volunteers clustered around Patrick Henry to see what he would do. Jubilantly, he took the money and signed the receipt. The volunteers began to chant, "All tyrants fear him! All free men adore him!" Patrick grinned and waved to his soldiers. He was enjoying every minute of the royal governor's capitulation. The bloodless victory tasted sweet.

Governor Dunmore was angry because he had been humiliated by an American from the backwoods. He despised the man. He denounced Patrick to the British government. "This Patrick Henry," he wrote, "is a desperate character who has been encouraging disobedience and exciting revolt for many years." And then Governor Dunmore did a foolish thing. He declared Patrick Henry an *outlaw*. He issued a proclamation: "No one in this colony is to aid or give help to one Patrick Henry, outlawed from the colony of Virginia because he, and his deluded followers, disturbed the peace of the colony."

Patrick's popularity skyrocketed to new heights. County after county sent him thanks. The Volunteer Company of Lancaster County answered Dunmore with a formal statement:

> Resolved: That every member of this Company return thanks to the worthy Captain Patrick Henry and the Volunteer Company of Hanover, for their spirited conduct on the late expedition, and they are determined to protect him from any insult that may be offered him on that account, at the risk of life and fortune.

Patrick's daughter Patsy was alarmed for his safety. "Papa, I'm afraid Lord Dunmore is after your scalp with a tomahawk. It frightens me." Patsy and her family had moved into Scotchtown to keep house for her father.

"Now, Patsy, Dunmore is only trying to bully me because I brought him to his knees. I'm not worried about any tomahawk that old buzzard wields."

Patsy was helping her father pack for his second journey to Philadelphia. Once again he was a delegate, this time to the Second Continental Congress. Suddenly Willie burst into the room. "Papa!" he yelled. "They're all here! They want you to hurry!"

"*Who* is here?" asked his father.

"Look out the window," Willie shouted. "Oh, it's great to have a father who's an outlaw!"

Patrick and Martha peered through the glass in astonishment. Gathered in the courtyard below was a large company of armed men on horseback.

"They've come to escort you safely across the border," said Willie. "Can I ride with you as far as Mrs. Hooe's ferry on the Potomac? Can I, Papa?"

"No, you must stay here and protect Scotchtown. You'll be the man in the family now, son."

Patrick's followers rode with him all the way to the Potomac River. When he got on the ferry to cross over to the Maryland shore, the men fired a salute. Cheer after cheer reached him across the water. The people loved Patrick Henry more than ever. They would never forget his daring march on Williamsburg.

It was Thomas Jefferson who noted in his records, "The first act of war in Virginia was led by Patrick Henry."

chapter 15

Commander-in-Chief . . . Without a Command

WHEN Patrick Henry arrived in Philadelphia, the Second Continental Congress was already meeting behind locked doors in the State House (later known as Independence Hall). The blood was not dry on the grass at Lexington and Concord, and at that very moment colonial troops were storming into Fort Ticonderoga. Yet war still had not been declared.

As he entered the hall, Patrick's eyes swept the beautiful white-paneled room lined with windows on two sides. Most of the same delegates had returned and once more Peyton Randolph presided. Suddenly Henry started. He could not believe what he saw. There sat Colonel George Washington dressed in the uniform of the Virginia Militia. The shoulders of his buff and blue coat were decorated with gold epaulets and a small sword hung at his side. The uniform, the determined bearing, and the serious expression, could mean only one thing. George Washington thought the business of this congress was war, not words.

Something else was new. Seated in an armchair on the

aisle was a portly man in a brown Quaker suit. He did
not wear a wig; his long gray hair fell to his shoulders.
Patrick Henry had never seen him before, but he recognized him at once. Printer, author, publisher, scientist,
inventor, businessman, linguist, philosopher, statesman
and friend to all humanity, Benjamin Franklin was America's most famous citizen.

As soon as the meeting adjourned, Patrick Henry introduced himself to the great man. "Dr. Franklin, sir, I want
to add my welcome to the others, and thank you for
your efforts in behalf of the colonies in England."

"You are too kind, Mr. Henry. I did not succeed in my
chief purpose. I wanted above all to keep America within
the British Empire. I failed. But I learned a lot. I've just
written a little pamphlet that may be helpful to the
British. It is called *Rules for Reducing a Great Empire
to a Small One*." The old man's face was serious, but his
eyes twinkled.

"Sir, I understand I have the honor of serving with you
on the Committee for Indian Friendship."

"Lord North has done an evil thing, Mr. Henry. He
told his agents to stop at nothing to get the six Indian
Nations to swing their bloody hatchets against us. The
more American scalps they bring in, the happier North
will be. Our committee must put a stop to this."

"There is just one man who can help us win the

friendship   of the Six Nations," Patrick Henry said quickly. "It is the Reverend Samuel Kirkland, a brave and beloved missionary to the Indians."

"And how will we get hold of him?"

"My Uncle Langloo — William Winston that is — is practically an Indian. He can find Kirkland."

"Good," said Franklin. "Get in touch with him at once. God helps those who help themselves, Mr. Henry."

Later Patrick Henry remarked to his old friend John Adams, "Isn't it odd Dr. Franklin, our wisest man, thinks he's a failure because he could not keep us in the British Empire?"

"At least one American is still firmly in the Empire," said Adams. "Franklin's son William, who used to be royal governor of New Jersey, has abandoned the American cause. He announced he will remain in England to the end of his days. His father is crushed."

"Franklin's son may have deserted him," said Patrick, "but his wit has not. I asked him about the boundary disputes between Virginia and Pennsylvania. He replied, 'Love your neighbors, Mr. Henry . . . but don't pull down your hedges.'"

"He's remarkable," Adams agreed. "Since he got back from England, he's started signing his letters B. Free Franklin."

Patrick Henry stood up in the Second Continental Congress and once again sounded a trumpet call to arms, just as he had in St. John's Church eight weeks earlier. "Gentlemen," he said, "I bring you a message from the yeomen and planters of Virginia. These rugged Americans told me, 'We will never be taxed except by our own representatives. United we stand, divided we fall.'"

The delegates were stirred by his words, but not all the delegates. To Patrick Henry's disgust, John Jay and John Dickinson wanted to send *another* appeal to England. The congress voted for a "Humble Petition to His Majesty" begging for an end of hostilities. But they also voted to raise an army.

Who should lead the army? Some said John Hancock, the rich, patriotic, and popular Harvard graduate. Others said Charles Lee, a tall hawk-nosed fighter who married the daughter of a Seneca chief and was known as Chief Boiling Water. Everywhere Lee went a pack of hound dogs and an uproar of confusion followed him. But John Hancock was handicapped by his enormous appetite for popularity, and General Charles Lee was born in England and had served in the British army since he was twelve. Could he be trusted?

John Adams got to his feet and made a speech nominating George Washington. All eyes turned to the straight-backed giant in the buff and blue uniform. George Washington's presence was monumental. Always in control of himself, the secret of his superhuman power was his ability to keep a demon temper in an iron cage. (Once or twice he let it go in a battle and became a wild man.) The portrait painter Gilbert Stuart said of him, "Had General Washington been born in the forests, he would have been the fiercest man among the savage tribes."

George Washington was unanimously elected Commander-in-Chief of the United Colonies.

Patrick jumped up and hurried over to congratulate his friend. Both men realized the risk in leading a rebellion against the king. There were tears in Washington's steel-blue eyes as he clasped Patrick Henry's hand and said, "Remember, Mr. Henry, what I now tell you. From this day, I date my fall and the ruin of my reputation."

Seldom has a man's prediction of his own future been so wrong.

Patrick Henry longed to be a military leader, too. He was in prime condition for military service and he knew he could handle men. Thirty-nine years old, a sturdy outdoor man, a strong horseman, and a fearless leader, Patrick was ready for combat.

As soon as congress adjourned, he hurried back to Virginia to join the army. He no longer worried about being an outlaw. The man who outlawed him had run away. Governor Dunmore was all smoke and no fire. He threatened to seize all property belonging to traitors. He threatened to free the slaves and reduce Williamsburg to ashes. But he knew he was not strong enough to do these things. And when Williamsburg became too hot for him, Dunmore fled to the safety of a British warship anchored in the blue York River.

At first, there seemed to be no obstacles in the way of Patrick Henry's budding military career. The most popular man in the colony, he was quickly elected Commander-in-Chief of Virginia's forces.

But the vote was not unanimous. Some people objected strenuously. "Why, Patrick Henry has had no military service," they exclaimed. The leader of the critics was that important gentleman and patriot, Edmund Pendleton. Pendleton wanted liberty, all right, but he also wanted law and order. He did not trust a boisterous man of the people like Patrick Henry.

It was finally agreed that all of Colonel Henry's decisions had to be checked by the Committee of Public Safety. The chairman of the committee was none other than the cautious Edmund Pendleton. This requirement made things difficult for Commander-in-Chief Henry.

The new army was an amazing sight. Men from every county in Virginia hurried to Colonel Henry's Williamsburg encampment behind William and Mary College. Trappers in buckskin and farmers in homespun

rubbed elbows with rich gentlemen in splendid uniforms. Some of the volunteers were only thirteen years old, but they were armed with short carbines. The Culpepper Marines carried a rattlesnake flag and wore scalping knives and tomahawks. They were dressed in coonskin hats and green hunting shirts, with LIBERTY OR DEATH painted in white letters across their chests. One joker said "Liberty or Death" was too strong for him, but he'd be glad to wear "Liberty or Be Crippled."

Colonel Patrick Henry, handsome in a smart new uniform, strode through camp inspecting the troops. Everyone knew him and he called most of the men by name. Patrick Henry had a genius for remembering names.

One day Henry spotted a handsome gentleman in a smooth white wig and salmon-colored coat watching the soldiers drill. He recognized John Randolph, "John the Tory," people called him. (His brother was known as "Peyton the Patriot.") Patrick went over to speak to Randolph. They had often been fierce rivals in court and they were miles apart in politics, but neither man carried a grudge.

"Mr. Randolph, sir, a pleasure to see you."

"Mr. Henry," John Randolph bowed slightly. He waved a graceful arm toward the soldiers. "This is to me a painful sight. The sword of battle has been drawn and heaven alone knows when it will be sheathed. There is no retreat for either side. He who has no retreat must conquer or die."

"And what are your plans, Mr. Randolph?"

"I do not take to rebellion the way you and my brother Peyton do. Following the dictates of *reason*, I shall remain loyal to England. I leave for England by the first packet."

"You will be missed, sir, especially by your friend General Washington and your cousin Tom Jefferson."

"I'm leaving my violin with Tom." John Randolph looked wistful. "We spent many happy hours together at the palace, fiddling with Francis Fauquier. But those days are gone forever. Mr. Henry, the Virginia of culture and charm, of fox hunting and horse racing, of house parties and happy times has vanished. I am going home."

Patrick kicked the dust with his boots. "To me, Virginia is still the best place on earth. I *am* home."

"I have to leave behind me my most precious possession," John Randolph said bitterly. "You, Mr. Henry, have infected my son, Edmund, with your 'liberty or death' talk. He insists on staying here."

Silently, the two men shook hands. There was no anger between them, just sadness. Each had made his decision. One to be an Englishman; the other an American. In every colony, families and friends split apart on the same rocky decision.

Colonel Henry met with small success as an army officer. A commander-in-chief is supposed to be distant and exclusive. But the "loneliness of high rank" was not for

Patrick Henry. He was one of the men, a fact that displeased the dignified Mr. Pendleton and his Committee of Public Safety.

Some people complained that Colonel Henry was not even serious enough. An officer named Lawson came to Patrick for advice. Lawson's affairs were in incredibly bad shape. He made a full statement of all his troubles, going into endless detail. After listening to the long list of difficulties, Henry was silent.

"Colonel Henry, what do you think I should do?" Lawson demanded.

Pulling a long face, Patrick said: "Why, faith, Lawson, you'd better run away."

Even Patrick's good friend General Washington doubted his military ability. "I think my Virginia countrymen made a capital mistake," Washington wrote, "when they took Henry out of the senate to place him in the field, and pity it is that he does not see this and resign."

At last the day came for the Virginians to go into action. Flags waved and drums rattled . . . but bitter disappointment awaited Colonel Henry. He discovered he was commander-in-chief on paper only. The combat assignment was given to his next-in-command, Colonel William Woodford. Pendleton thought that a man like Colonel Woodford, a veteran of the French and Indian

Wars, was safer. Everyone had trouble controlling the undisciplined militia, even George Washington, and Henry was anything but strict.

Pendleton sent Woodford to Norfolk, where the fighting was. Colonel Woodford won an important battle at Great Bridge, throwing Commander-in-Chief Henry still further in the shade. One rebuff followed another, until Woodford was reporting directly to Pendleton, paying no attention whatsoever to Patrick Henry.

The crowning blow came on the last day of February, 1776, when the Committee of Safety sent for Colonel Henry. With some misgiving, Patrick strode into the capital, the building where he had enjoyed so many triumphs as a Burgess.

Around the polished table in the Council Chamber sat the committee. Mr. Pendleton, looking elegant in an elaborately curled wig, occupied the royal governor's armchair.

"Colonel Henry," Pendleton said briskly, "our state militia is to become part of the continental forces. We are happy to offer you a commission as colonel in the Continental Army. Andrew Lewis will be our brigadier general."

Lewis was to be promoted over the Commander-in-Chief! This was the end.

Patrick Henry bowed. When he pulled himself up straight, all expression was drained from his face. "Thank you for your consideration. I regret, however, I must decline. Tomorrow I shall retire to Scotchtown."

The news of Colonel Henry's resignation spread quickly. His officers were outraged. They sent him a letter saying, "Your withdrawing yourself from service fills us with sorrow, as it deprives us of our father and leader. Yet we applaud your spirited resentment to so glaring an indignity."

The word *father* is a key word in the letter. It is one rarely used in the military. Patrick Henry's men loved him. The officers put on black mourning bands and marched to Henry's quarters. They insisted their colonel dine with them at the Raleigh Tavern.

It was a noisy, hearty dinner, with many sentimental speeches. The party lasted until the candles burned down into their sconces. Even Patrick Henry's eloquence could not console his men. "I am unhappy to part with you," he said in a touching farewell. "I leave the service, but I leave my heart with you. May God bless you and make you the glorious instruments of saving our country."

As he turned to leave, a great commotion broke out in the street below. Lieutenant John Marshall flung open the door of the Raleigh. Crowded around the steps of the tavern were the soldiers of the First Regiment. They were in a rebellious uproar. Most of them had enlisted because of Patrick Henry.

"We're leaving!" they shouted.

"Give us our discharge!"

"If Colonel Henry goes, we go!"

Patrick, now a civilian, turned to his good friend and brother-in-law, Colonel William Christian. "Order these men back to camp. Tell them I will talk to them there."

The enlisted men grumbled, but they obeyed orders. Back in camp their indignation boiled over again. They said they would never serve under any other commander. They threatened mutiny. Patrick Henry had to go from one group to another, quieting the men. "No one man matters," he told them. "We must each do what we are best fitted to do for the cause."

The truth was that Patrick Henry was not fitted to be a military man. He knew little about strategy and tactics. He disliked system and regularity and formality, and he made the mistake of treating his soldiers as equals. Sadly he realized his army career was ended. He never used the title of colonel again.

Patrick trotted old Shandy along the muddy road to Scotchtown. Pat's head bent low against the strong March wind, his chin touching his chest. A brooding melancholy stifled his spirit. His dreams of military glory were smashed, his pride bruised.

Even before he turned into Scotchtown, he sensed something was wrong. Patsy came out to break the news. His beloved Sarah was dead. Patrick laid his head on Shandy's mane and cried. His Sarah was gone.

In twenty-one years of marriage Sarah had given him three strong sons and three blooming daughters, but even they could not ease the pain in their father's heart. Sorrows seemed to gather around him as storm clouds around a mountain. He remembered the words of Jeremiah, read to him when he was a boy by the Reverend Samuel Davies:"They have healed also the hurt of the daughter of my people slightly, saying Peace, peace; when there is no peace."

Patrick Henry, the man of many words, fell silent. For days he barely spoke. The deeper the sorrow, the less tongue it has. These were his darkest hours.

chapter 16

The First Governor of Virginia

THE American colonies advanced along a highroad strewn with corpses and wet with blood, toward total separation from England. Patrick Henry was elected to the Virginia convention to consider the burning question of the day. Should the American colonies declare their independence from the mother country? Each colony had to decide for itself.

All the old leaders gathered at the convention in Williamsburg, with two exceptions. George Washington was fighting in the field, and Peyton Randolph had died of a stroke at a dinner party in Philadelphia. One new delegate attracted attention by his short stature and broad intelligence. Young James Madison, just four years out of Princeton, was already on the way to a great career. (Years later Madison married Patrick Henry's cousin Dolly Payne — twenty-seven years younger than he — and became the fourth President of the United States.)

Controversy raged strong and hot, for independence and against. To everyone's amazement, Patrick Henry threw cold water on the impatient hotheads. "Independence, yes," he said, "but first, the colonies must unify and, second, we need help from Spain and France. We are too young and weak to stand alone."

His followers were shocked. They could not imagine Patrick Henry wanting *delay*. Debate burned hotter and hotter. Skillfully, Patrick Henry led the argument exactly where he wanted it to go. Little by little it became clear what he was doing. The great actor was beating the bushes to drive out the timid. As soon as he got people arguing against him, he switched sides. What he really wanted (and the resolution is still preserved in his own handwriting) was "an immediate, clear, and full declaration of independence."

Edmund Randolph wrote to his Tory father, John Randolph, now the guest of Lord Dunmore in Scotland: "Mr. Henry became a pillar of fire leading others through darkness to the promised land. The inflamed convention followed him. His eloquence unlocked the secret springs of the human heart, robbed danger of its terror, and broke the keystone in the arch of royal power."

At last the day came for the vote on independence. People crowded under the windows of the capitol, straining to hear the count. One young man, standing on another's shoulders, suddenly yelled, "Unanimous!"

The crowd let out a shout of joy. On top of the capitol, men hauled the British flag down from the clock tower, balled it up, and threw it on the ground. The excited crowd hooted and hollered. As the flag of St. George was hoisted to the top of the pole, fifes and drums rattled and people shouted.

May 15, 1776, was Williamsburg's "Little Fourth of July." It was a glorious celebration. The Army of Virginia paraded proudly under General Andrew Lewis. Patrick Henry felt a pang when he watched his former comrades swing past. Fireworks crackled, bells rang, people cheered. Overexcited patriots even threw rocks at the governor's palace and toppled Governor Botetourt's statue from its pedestal. *America, behold your friend,* the inscription read. And there he lay on the grass, his nose chipped, his robes battered.

The next day Patrick Henry and all the other leaders attended a special service in Bruton Parish Church. They offered prayers for the independent state of Virginia, for the great Congress of the separate states, and for General Washington and the victory of American arms.

Then the members of the Virginia convention sat down to write out a state constitution, to replace Virginia's royal charter. As soon as the meeting was called to order, Thomas Jefferson stood up and objected. "We were not sent here to make a constitution," he said. "To write a constitution, we have to be legally elected for just that purpose."

George Wythe seconded his former student.

Patrick Henry said, "We were elected for a general, not a specific purpose. It is not only all right, but *necessary* for this convention to frame a constitution."

George Mason and Edmund Pendleton backed up Henry. The delegates voted to proceed.

Once again Patrick Henry crossed swords with Tom Jefferson. Their friendship was by now pretty well cut up. This time the sensitive Jefferson was hurt. He felt his legal knowledge had been tossed aside.

Drafting a constitution was hard work. Patrick wrote a discouraged letter to his friend John Adams.

> Williamsburg
> May 20, 1776

My dear Sir:

Our convention is now employed in the great work of forming a constitution. My republican form has many enemies. Our sessions are very long and I cannot count on my supporters. Would you and your Sam Adams were here!

Let me beg to be presented to my ever-esteemed S. Adams. Adieu, my dear sir. May God preserve you, and give you every good thing.

> P. Henry

P. S. Will you and S. A. now and then write?

John Adams wrote back from Philadelphia on June 3rd: "Happy Virginia, whose constitution is to be framed by so masterly a builder as Patrick Henry!"

The Virginians, still smarting from the strong power of the royal governors, wanted to make the head of their new state almost powerless. Patrick Henry begged them to give the governor a veto. They would not consider it. Virginia's governor could only serve three years in a row, and he had to be re-elected every year. Patrick's enemies — and Jefferson was not the only one who differed with him — whispered that Henry thought he was going to be the first governor and he wanted all the power he could get. Some said he dreamed of becoming a dictator.

At last the new Commonwealth of Virginia had a constitution. It was so successful that it became a model for others. It began with the statement, "All men are by nature equally free and independent." When these words reached Lord North in London he laughed and said, "I could never agree with such an *absurd* idea."

Meanwhile, in Philadelphia, a mover and a shaker named Tom Paine wrote a booklet called *Common Sense,* urging a declaration of independence by all the colonies. One hundred thousand copies were sold. Soon people in every colony quoted Paine and demanded independence. Paine, a poor corset-maker befriended by Benjamin Franklin,

was a fiery genius with heavy black eyebrows, a long
nose, wild hair and wilder eyes. It was he who first coined
the words United States of America.

The Continental Congress appointed a committee of
five to draft a statement of independence. Patrick's one-
time friend, Thomas Jefferson, wrote the brilliant Declaration of Independence. Jefferson was not only one of the
builders of the new nation. He was the one who best
stated the *reason why* it should be.

When old Ben Franklin signed this historic document,
he expressed the danger that haunted it. "We must indeed all hang together," he said, "or most assuredly we
shall all hang separately."

The first Fourth of July touched off another great celebration. Guns banged, skyrockets sizzled, people sang,
cheered, cried. There were banquets, balls, bonfires, il-
luminations and every other kind of festivity, to celebrate
the birth of the United States.

The next day, July 5, 1776, Patrick Henry was over-
whelmingly elected the first governor of the state of Virginia. Directly after taking the oath of office, he left
Williamsburg to return to Scotchtown. He wanted to put
his affairs in order before moving into the governor's
palace.

The hot July sun beat down on Patrick and Caesar as

they trotted along the dusty road. Patrick pulled Shandy to a halt. He stripped off his damp coat and tossed it to his slave. "I never felt such heat," he said, mopping his face.

"Mr. Patrick, you look all red and splotchy-like. Maybe us better take a rest on the riverbank."

"Poppycock, Caesar. You're thirty-nine, the same as I am, and you don't need to rest."

Caesar laughed. "Mr. Patrick, next to Africa, where I was born, this here weather's freezing."

Before long Patrick checked his horse again. "Caesar, give me that coat. This sun must be dropping fast. I'm cold."

Caesar rolled his eyes. "Mr. Patrick, 'tain't cooler, it's hotter. Sumpin's powerful wrong with you."

Patrick shrugged and buttoned up his coat. He pulled the collar up around his neck and spurred his horse into a gallop. By the time Scotchtown loomed up before him, his head was throbbing like a drum. Caesar helped his master up the stairs and into bed.

Thoroughly alarmed, Patsy, Betsy, and Anne sent for Dr. Dabney. They had never seen their father sick before. The doctor took one look at the shivering patient and shook his head. "Malaria!"

The girls began to cry. Malaria was a frightening ill-

ness, and in colonial times no one knew how to cure the
disease. Once malaria got in the blood, it stayed there. It
was often fatal.

Patrick's three daughters nursed him with devotion
and skill. His strong body responded to their care. Four
weeks later the Williamsburg *Gazette* published welcome
news:

> We have the pleasure to inform the public that our
> worthy Governor, who is now at his seat in Hanover, is
> so much recovered that he walks out daily, and it is
> hoped he will soon be able to return to his high and im-
> portant office.

By the middle of September, Patrick Henry and his six
children packed to move to Williamsburg. Dr. Dabney
hated to see his patient go. "Look here, Governor, Williamsburg is low, mosquito-ridden country. I'd like you to
stay in Hanover until the first frost."

"If I come apart again, Dabney," the deep eyes were
laughing, "I'll fetch you to put me together. I think you
could put scrambled eggs back into the shell if you
wanted to."

Patrick Henry was excited when he stepped out of his
carriage at the grilled gate of the governor's palace, lord
and master of all he surveyed. He paused to look up at
the stone lion and unicorn on top of the gateposts, and

recall Robert Carter Nicholas's remark: "They are here, Mr. Henry, to remind us we are British." How odd that the British left their symbols behind to welcome the first American governor.

After Lord Dunmore fled, the palace had been used as a hospital. It was a good deal the worse for wear, but Patrick's children pronounced it perfect. "Papa," cried Patsy, "do you realize we have ten different gardens? There's a fruit garden, and a rose —"

"Have you seen the maze, Papa?" interrupted Willie. "It's made out of holly hedges and you chase round and round and *never* come out."

"The bowling green is splendid, Father," said John. "It's like the ones in Scotland Grandfather used to talk about." John, now a man of twenty-one, wore his buff and blue army uniform. He would soon leave to join General Washington's troops.

"Papa, you must go right to bed. Remember what Dr. Dabney said."

Patrick looked at his favorite daughter through misty eyes. "Patsy, my dear, you sound just like your mother . . . I mean the way she used to sound."

The first night in the governor's palace was a bad one for Patrick. He could not sleep at all. He kept remembering how Governor Botetourt looked when he lay dying in that same canopied bed.

Some aristocrats — and all the Tories — laughed at the idea of a hotheaded countryman like Patrick Henry presiding in the "royal" palace. But Patrick surprised his critics. He turned out to be a dignified governor. Always an actor, he even looked the part. He put away his plain clothes and dressed in a suit of black velvet. In cool weather he threw over his shoulders a dramatic scarlet cloak. Patrick Henry no longer tramped the trails with his dog and gun but rode in a state carriage drawn by four horses. When he smiled and waved, the people thought he was wonderful.

The first governor took over in a time of crisis. Tories plotted mischief within the state and war raged in the north. From Valley Forge, George Washington wrote Governor Henry:

> We can scarcely count on any supplies and the goods
> on hand are so nearly consumed that I look with greatest
> concern on the sufferings of the soldiers for the remainder
> of this year, and as for the next, I view them as naked,
> unless clothing is collected.

General Washington wrote again and again asking for money and supplies. Patrick reached into the back country to meet the demands. He even sent all the cattle he could find, to feed the ragged Continentals at Valley Forge. Soon Governor Henry had stripped Virginia of arms and provisions. A cry of protest went up. "Virginia is unarmed," people said bitterly. "Never mind about General Washington — we're in danger from the British ourselves."

"Of course we are in danger," Governor Henry agreed. "But if Washington is wiped out at Valley Forge, we're *finished*."

Meanwhile, George Washington called his shivering soldiers together. He had learned from Patrick Henry the power of *words*. As his men stood in the snow, some of them bleeding and barefoot, Washington read aloud the stirring words from Tom Paine's new pamphlet, "The Crisis."

> These are the times that try men's souls. The summer soldier and the sunshine patriot will, in this crisis, shrink from the service of their country. . . . Tyranny, like hell, is not easily conquered. . . . He whose heart is firm will pursue his principles unto death.

In these darkest days of the war, a group of treacherous Tories and discouraged patriots hatched a plot to overthrow George Washington as Commander-in-Chief. Governor Henry received an anonymous letter asking him to join the scurrilous plot. "Throw this letter in the fire," the unknown traitor wrote.

Instead of throwing it in the fire, Governor Henry dispatched it by swift messenger to General Washington. No one knew better than Patrick Henry that it was George Washington who held the whole desperate war effort together. The battle cry of his weary soldiers was *Washington, or no army!*

Henry's action may have saved Washington. One of the few times George Washington dropped his chilly dignity was when he wrote to thank Governor Henry for warning him of danger.

All during the war, Patrick Henry was plagued by malaria. One attack of the fever was so bad he had to return to Scotchtown to recuperate. He pretended it was all Dr. Dabney's fault. "Drat it, Dabney," he thundered, "health is wealth, and thanks to you, I'm poverty-stricken."

"Now, now, Governor, take your quinine and keep quiet. Don't excite yourself."

"We are living through the most crucial days of our history and you say 'don't excite yourself!'" Patrick imitated the doctor's voice. He sounded so funny that Caesar doubled up with laughter. "You might just as well say to a waterfall, 'Don't splash.'"

One day an extraordinary young man cantered up to Scotchtown to call on the governor. He was a tall, sunburned ranger dressed in buckskin. His name was George Rogers Clark.

"Governor Henry, sir," said Clark, "I've just ridden in

from the county of Kentucky. The people out there sent me because they need help, and need it bad."

"Indians?"

"Yes, sir. The British are giving the Indians guns, liquor, and leadership. They whip 'em up and set 'em on the Kentuckians. It's fierce."

Patrick Henry was impressed by the young athlete with

the long nose and strong face. George Rogers Clark was his kind of man.

"Mr. Clark, I happen to know Americans are also trying to fire up the Indians to attack the British. The Indians must be thoroughly confused."

"I've heard you are sympathetic to the Indians, Governor."

"I am. Just recently I entertained some Indian chiefs at the palace," Patrick chuckled. "They kept their feather bonnets on in the house. It upset the servants."

Clark smiled politely. "Sir, this situation is desperate. Chief Dragging Canoe is leading the Cherokees along a bloody warpath. He keeps the British 'hair buyers' well supplied with American scalps. The people in Kentucky County are Virginians, sir. They say they are forgotten Virginians."

"Exactly what do they need?"

"Five hundred pounds of gunpowder. It will take all of that, Governor Henry, to save Kentucky from Indian massacre."

"By heaven, you shall have it! Take the gunpowder to Kentucky with my blessing. Mr. Clark, the future of America depends on men like you."

chapter 17

Mistress Dorothea Dandridge

ONE fine autumn evening Governor Henry and his friend Richard Henry Lee strolled out the palace gates to call on George Wythe, whose large brick house faced the Palace Green. It seemed like an ordinary evening. But for Patrick Henry it turned out to be most extraordinary.

A handsomely dressed slave led the visitors into Wythe's study, a high-ceilinged room with whitewashed walls and an elaborate needlework rug. George Wythe was sitting near the stone fireplace playing chess with young Edmund Randolph.

"Your excellency!" exclaimed Wythe, rising to welcome his guests. "I am honored."

"Mr. Wythe, that title sounds a little British. Plain 'governor' will do for me. We're interrupting your game?"

"Indeed not . . . Governor." Wythe smiled slightly. "Join us by the fire."

The four men sat around the hearth and chatted pleasantly. Weighed down with war worries, they talked about small things — of Williamsburg's first bathtub, recently installed in the St. George Tucker house across the way, of the fishpond Governor Henry had made by damming the western end of the palace brook. "But the poor fish are too civilized," Patrick complained. "Not like the trout I used to pull out of the South Anna and the Paumunkey."

The conversation turned to books and Richard Henry Lee took over. He talked on and on and on about his favorite book, *Don Quixote*. Finally Governor Henry yawned and rose from his armchair, "You overlooked one of the finest things in the book, Lee."

"What's that, Governor?"

"When Sancho Panza says, 'Blessed be the man that first invented sleep. It covers me all over, like a cloak.'"

The men laughed, Lee not quite as heartily as the rest.

Patrick turned to go . . . and there she was. She stood in the doorway, dressed in a cloud of pale pink. Her dark hair and dark eyes shone in the candlelight. He never forgot how she looked at that moment.

Wythe took her by the hand and said, "Governor Henry, may I present our guest, Mistress Dorothea Dandridge?"

"Mr. Henry, I'm so happy to see you again. Oh dear, I guess I should say *Your Excellency*."

"We've known each other too long for that foolishness, Dolly." Patrick put his hand in his pocket and pulled out a tattered piece of green felt. "Mr. Wythe, your house guest and I are old friends. She made this penwiper for me when she was a little girl. It was a prize for winning the Parson's Case. I've carried it for luck ever since."

Dorothea lowered her eyes and blushed slightly. Patrick Henry thought he had never seen anything so charming.

"Last I heard, Miss Dolly, you were about to marry John

Paul Jones. Is that wild swashbuckler still cutting capers for your approval?"

Dolly's laugh sounded like a spring brook. "When Mr. Jones departed to fight the British on the high seas, he left with my blessing."

Patrick grinned. Then he realized he must maintain his dignity. He said good night and left. He felt as if he were walking on air.

The very next afternoon Governor Henry returned to Wythe House. This time he did not come to call on George Wythe.

He and Mistress Dandridge sipped tea in the Wythes' parlor. "As near as I can figure," Patrick said bluntly, "you must be about twenty, Miss Dolly."

"Twenty-one. But, sir," Dorothea's dark eyes lit up with mischief, "you know a gentleman never discusses a lady's age."

"Confound it, Dolly, then I'm no gentleman. Your age matters to me. You know how old I am? Forty-one. Exactly twenty years older than you. My father said no wise man ever wishes to be younger. Wise or otherwise, right now I'd like to be twenty-two."

"Mr. Henry, age does not depend on years. Some men are born old, some never grow old."

Patrick smiled. Miss Dorothea Dandridge had a talent for saying the right thing. "My mother used to teach me

Shakespeare. When I was a little boy, she made me stand on a chair and recite Adam's words in *As You Like It.* 'Though I look old, yet I am strong and lusty, for in my youth I never did apply hot and rebellious liquors in my blood.' She wanted me never to take a drink — and I still don't drink anything stronger than spring water."

"That reminds me of a song, Governor. Let me play it for you." Dorothea slipped into the chair before the harpsichord and began to play. She was an accomplished musician and she sang in a pure sweet voice *Drink to Me Only with Thine Eyes.* Her large dark eyes looked deeply into Patrick's blue ones. The Governor of Virginia felt his head swim and his knees buckle. *It's only the old malaria,* he told himself. But he knew better.

It was a whirlwind courtship. Dorothea Dandridge, young, beautiful, rich, and aristocratic, could have her choice of all the eligible men in the state. She chose Governor Patrick Henry, a widower old enough to be her father. Patrick Henry never got over it. He adored her and she returned his affection.

Williamsburg was agog over the governor's romance. "Pat's *some* picker," the people chuckled.

The wedding was to be held in Bruton Parish, the old church of salmon-colored brick built by Dorothea's grandfather, the royal governor Alexander Spotswood. The Reverend Patrick Henry made the journey from Hanover to perform the ceremony. Although he was old and ill (he died that very year), Uncle Patrick could not miss this occasion.

Bruton Parish, with its pale oyster-colored walls, high clear glass windows, and gray-green flagstone floor, was a perfect place for a wedding. Uncle Patrick had only one objection. "Patrick," he scolded his unpredictable nephew, "am I to understand you have let the prisoners out of jail, so they can pump the church organ at your wedding?"

Patrick laughed out loud at his uncle's shocked expression. "Our organist, Peter Pelham, keeps the jail in his spare time. These aren't ordinary prisoners, Uncle Patrick. They're trained organ-pumpers."

The day of the governor's wedding seemed like a holiday in Williamsburg. Because of the war, Patrick tried to keep the ceremony and festivities fairly quiet. He did not succeed. It was a happy celebration and everyone took part, the aristocrats, the common people, and the slaves. Patrick only remembered two things. The way Dorothea looked when she came down the aisle on the arm of Colonel Dandridge, her dark hair piled high under a veil of lace and her creamy skin matching the gardenias she carried. The other picture was Uncle Langloo escorting Patrick's mother to her seat. The bridegroom struggled to keep from laughing. Langloo had bought a white wig to grace the occasion, but it did not fit. It had slipped slightly askew, and Langloo was perspiring heavily. He looked like a snow-capped mountain during a spring thaw.

Proudly and happily, Patrick carried his young bride over the threshold of the governor's palace. Despite her youth, Dolly seemed at home there. She made a gracious hostess and presided over the palace with ease.

We know exactly what Patrick Henry expected of a wife, because he wrote it all down in a letter to his daughter Anne when she married Spencer Roane.

> The first maxim you should impress on your mind is never to attempt to control your husband by anger. A man of sense and warm feelings cannot and will not bear opposition attended by an angry look. A husband expects from his wife smiles, not frowns. A difference with your husband ought to be considered the greatest calamity. It is a demon which must never be permitted to enter the home.

We do not know if the new Mrs. Henry lived up to this high standard, but we do know that Patrick and his charming Dolly spent twenty-two unusually happy years together. They had four daughters — Dorothea, Sara (named for Patrick's mother and his first wife), Martha, and Catherine — and seven sons — Patrick, Fayette, Alexander Spotswood, Nathaniel (named for Dolly's father), Richard, Edward Winston, and John. The fact that Patrick already had by his first wife children named Martha and John did not seem to bother anyone.

It was lucky Governor Henry had a beautiful young wife and a growing family to divert him, because he was worried by countless problems. Being a state governor during the American Revolution was difficult. In those days, the state government was far more important than the weak federal government.

Virginia needed so many things. There were troops to raise; guns and gunpowder to manufacture; salt, lead and medicine to import. And all this had to be done in the face of opposition from a third of the population, the Loyalists who believed America had no business fighting the British at all.

Hanging over everything was the ever-present Indian menace. As governor, Patrick was supposed to protect all of Virginia, a vast unexplored territory which was presumed to stretch to the Pacific Ocean. The Indians gave him constant trouble. The Shawnees were the worst. Their majestic chief, Cornstalk, knew the white man could not be trusted. Cornstalk was an orator who could speak almost as well as Patrick Henry. With princely dignity he rebuked the Virginians:

For many years this was our land. Then you came and took it for your own. You plowed our prairie. Now the buffalo and deer no longer graze there, and my people go hungry. You do not care. You do not keep your word. Still you ask us to keep the truce. No defense is left to the brave Shawnee, except to fight.

At dawn one day Cornstalk and his Shawnees crossed the Ohio and attacked the settlers at Point Pleasant. All day the bloody battle raged. By dusk, although two hundred whites were dead or wounded, the Indians decided to retreat. Later, peace talks were held under a flag of truce. Some angry settlers brewed an evil scheme and Chief Cornstalk was treacherously murdered.

When Governor Henry heard of the murder, his normally gentle nature exploded in anger. "Is there no end to this senseless slaughter?" he bellowed. "The Americans are stronger than the Indians and we are supposed to be smarter. We *must* take leadership. There will never be any progress so long as we sink to the bloody level of savages. Cornstalk was a great leader. Now we will have to live with the vengeful spirit of the Shawnees. His braves will be seeking bloody revenge for the rest of their lives, and I do not blame them!"

Some colonists muttered, "Governor Henry is an Indian-lover." And some of them said worse things than that. Patrick Henry even changed his own tune somewhat, after his brother-in-law, Colonel William Christian,

was scalped by Indian warriors in Kentucky. Governor
Henry sent a strong letter to Congress saying it was the
duty of the confederation to protect the frontier. But by
and large, Patrick Henry understood the Indians and took
the lead in demanding justice for them.

One day a frontiersman asked if he could see Governor
Henry about "an urgent matter in the west." Patrick sent
word for him to come in. The governor put down his pen
and pushed his reading glasses up on his forehead. Standing before his desk was George Rogers Clark. This time
Clark did not wear hunting clothes. He was dressed in the
uniform of a colonel in the Continental Army. He took off
his cocked hat and bowed.

"Governor Henry, sir, may I request a private audience
with you? I wish to discuss a matter of great secrecy."

Behind closed doors, Colonel Clark unfolded a daring
scheme. It was nothing less than a plot to conquer all the
British forts north of the Ohio.

Patrick Henry leaned forward, his face eager with excitement. He was well acquainted with the known geog-
raphy, rivers, soil and climate of Virginia, and he longed
to explore the unknown. Colonel Clark was talking to the
right man.

"What you propose, Colonel Clark, is an incredible un-
dertaking. What makes you think you can do it?"

"Sir, my men and I have already scouted the British

forts from Kaskaskia to the Wabash River, in the Illinois country. We have full information on them. We know how to work silently and strike swiftly. We know how to enlist the aid of the Indians. If we get help from Black-bird, the great Chippewa chief, we might even capture Detroit. My scouts tell me it is poorly defended." Clark's voice rang with authority.

"Colonel Clark, your plan is staggering. I will have to consult my advisers." George Rogers Clark looked alarmed.

"Don't worry, we'll maintain secrecy. My dear Colonel Clark, men who have plotted revolution understand the danger of a careless tongue."

Governor Henry called in for council George Wythe, Thomas Jefferson, and George Mason. He chose his ad-visers well. Except for Wythe, these men were plungers. They knew that to win all, you have to gamble all. And in their enthusiasm, they pulled Wythe right along with them.

After the conference, Governor Henry sent these in-structions to George Rogers Clark:

Williamsburg
January 2, 1778

Colonel Clark:

You are to proceed with all convenient speed to raise seven companies of soldiers, of 50 men each, officered and armed most properly, and with this force attack the British Forts at Kaskasky. You are to apply to General Hand for the necessary powder and lead.

If you are so fortunate as to succeed in your expedition, you will take every possible measure to secure all the British artillery and stores.

For transportation you are to apply to the commanding officer at Fort Pitt for boats. You are to take special care to keep the true destination of your force secret. Its success depends upon this.

It is earnestly desired that you show humanity to such British subjects and other persons as fall in your hands. You are in no instant to depart from the humanity that has hitherto distinguished the Americans.

This was an important decision. Had it not been for the men of vision who supported George Rogers Clark, the man of action, the states of Ohio, Indiana, Illinois, and Wisconsin might today belong to Canada.

When Patrick Henry's third term as governor came to an end, many people wanted to change the law which said no man could be elected more than three times in a row. The Tories started a rumor that Henry planned to make himself a dictator. Mr. Archibald Cary stopped Patrick's stepbrother, John Syme, on Duke of Gloucester Street and shouted, "I hear your brother wants to be a dictator. Tell him that the day he tries it will be the day of his death, for he shall feel my dagger in his heart before sunset."

When Patrick Henry heard this threat he just laughed. He had already forbidden all attempts to change the election law. With chilly formality he welcomed Thomas Jefferson as the second governor of Virginia. Then he and Dolly and the children left the hurly-burly of Williamsburg for the peace of Leatherwood, a large estate he had bought in Henry County, the county named after him. He hated to sell Scotchtown, his home so full of memories, but his doctors thought higher country, with pure air and pure spring water, might help his recurring bouts with malaria.

Leatherwood was set on a wild tract of land within sight of the Blue Ridge Mountains. Patrick liked living on the edge of the wilderness. He watched the mountains change color with the shifting shadows, and he longed to cross over them. Half pathfinder and half pioneer, he dressed in leather breeches made by his mother (a lost art, at which she excelled) and lived out of doors as much as he could. But the malaria did not improve. It got worse.

chapter 18

Patrick Henry vs. Thomas Jefferson

THREE months after Patrick Henry's retirement from office, he was elected to the state legislature. Once again he journeyed to Williamsburg; but this time he did not stay. The British invaded Virginia and the entire government fled to Charlottesville in the Blue Ridge Mountains.

General Cornwallis was eager to capture the leaders of Virginia. He sent a swift striking force after them, commanded by Sir Banastre Tarleton. Tarleton was one of the real villains of the Revolution. He led a troop of prize cutthroats, British soldiers, and Tory volunteers who wore green uniforms and rode stolen horses. Everywhere they went, they spread terror by their wholesale butchery of the Americans.

Tarleton and his green-coated rascals might have wiped out Governor Jefferson and his government, had they not galloped past the Cuckoo Tavern and awakened one Captain John Jouette. Jouette spied the mounted troop from a window and realized what was up. He jumped on his horse and took a short cut to Charlottesville.

At 4:30 A.M. Governor Jefferson, who liked to rise with the sun, saw a horseman streaking up his driveway.

"Good heavens, Jouette," he cried, "what is it?"

"The British, sir," panted Jouette, "they're coming!"

"Warn the gentlemen of the legislature," said Jefferson. "I'll take my family to the farm in Bedford."

Two hours later Sir Banastre Tarleton came thundering into Charlottesville. But the government of Virginia had vanished.

Gallant Jack Jouette was later presented with a pair of pistols and a sword by the men of the legislature whose lives he had saved.

Patrick Henry escaped from the raiders with Benjamin Harrison and two others. Late in the day, tired and hungry, the four men stopped their horses at a small hut in a gorge to ask for food. The old woman who came to the door was hostile. "Ride on!" she said. "You'll get nothing from me. My husband and sons have gone to Charlottesville to fight for you . . . and you running away as fast as you can."

"Madam," said Patrick Henry, "this is Mr. Benjamin Harrison, the Speaker of the House. You don't think he'd have left if it wasn't necessary, do you?"

"I always thought well of Mr. Harrison till now," answered the old woman. "He has no business to run from the enemy."

"What would you say if Patrick Henry had fled with the rest of us?" asked Harrison.

"Patrick Henry! I'd tell you there wasn't a word of truth in it. He'd never do such a cowardly thing."

"Madam," said Benjamin Harrison, with his most courtly flourish, "may I present to you the former governor of Virginia and the leader of our legislature, Mr. Patrick Henry?"

The old woman threw her apron up over her face. When she pulled it down, she was red with embarrassment. She made a low curtsy. "If you are Mr. Patrick Henry, it must be all right. Enter, gentlemen, and welcome to the best I have."

It was more than a month after the Tarleton Raid before the government returned to the capital. By that time Thomas Jefferson had resigned as governor and John Page was elected to take his place.

Thomas Jefferson had a bad time of it as governor of Virginia. A crisis was reached when the traitor Benedict Arnold, now a general in the British army, sailed up the James River with eight hundred men. Arnold burned Richmond and ravaged much of Virginia. Indignation flared up against Governor Jefferson. People said he had not prepared Virginia for attack.

Patrick Henry was on a committee that tried to investigate Jefferson's conduct as governor. Always sensitive to criticism, Jefferson was indignant. To have his actions questioned by his boyhood friend was intolerable. As far as he was concerned, it was the end. Abruptly and bitterly, Jefferson terminated their long friendship. Patrick Henry was saddened but he was not surprised, for over the years their misunderstandings had multiplied.

This was the lowest point in the public career of Thomas Jefferson. Unlike the popular Patrick, Jefferson knew he had no chance to be re-elected governor. Disheartened, he returned to Monticello and wrote *Notes on the State of Virginia,* pouring out his bitterness against Patrick Henry. He even revived the old rumor that Patrick wanted to make himself a dictator.

The contrast between these two former friends is fascinating. Jefferson was a genius, a scholar, and a cultivated gentleman; Henry was a rough outdoor man, untutored, except for his reading of Latin and the Bible. Jefferson was shy and self-contained; Henry was warm and outgoing. Jefferson resented criticism of any kind; Henry did not give a hoot what people thought of him. Jefferson was a poor speaker, but he was one of our greatest writers; Henry was a marvelous orator but he wrote almost nothing. He did not even write out his speeches. Jefferson said, "Patrick Henry throws himself into a sentence and trusts Almighty God to get him out." Jefferson had a hot redheaded temper; Henry was slow to anger.

Jefferson loved solitude and seclusion; Henry, born with
a knack for getting along with people, was almost never
alone. Thomas Jefferson believed in the theory of democracy, but he was actually a little aloof; Henry practiced
democracy by being one with the people. Jefferson
was a man of the world who had lived in Europe. He
dressed elegantly and knew a lot about French cooking
and French wine; Henry never traveled farther from Virginia than Philadelphia and New York. He liked plain
food, plain clothes and plain water. Jefferson had a highly
cultivated sense of beauty, especially in music and ar-
chitecture; Henry thought beauty was a by-product of nature. Jefferson was a brilliant author, architect, inventor,
scientist, linguist, musician, political and legal philosopher.
Patrick Henry distrusted theorists and bookworms. He
was a quick-witted man of action, a born leader of men.

Despite all these differences, there were strong similari-
ties between the two. Both men were ambitious, humor-
ous, and imaginative. Both sacrificed their personal de-
sires for the needs of Virginia and, later, the nation. And
both of them embraced danger for the cause of American
freedom. Each in his own way devoted his life to the pur-
suit of liberty.

In 1803 William Wirt, who wrote the first biography of
Patrick Henry, asked Thomas Jefferson for his opinion of

the great orator. Jefferson was over sixty by then, and Patrick had been dead four years.

"Were I to give Henry's character in general terms," wrote Thomas Jefferson, now third President of the United States, "it would be of mixed aspect. I think he was the best humored man in society I almost ever knew, and the greatest orator that ever lived. He had a consummate knowledge of the human heart, which directed his eloquence and enabled him to gain a popularity with the people at large never perhaps equaled."

And then Thomas Jefferson took aim and fired. "Henry's judgment in other matters was inaccurate. In matters of law it was not worth a copper. He was avaricious and rotten-hearted. His two great passions were the love of money and the love of fame. When they came into competition, love of money won."

Rotten-hearted! After years of research, historians know this accusation is unjust. But President Jefferson's biting words severely damaged Patrick Henry's place in history.

At last the bloody revolution ended. General Washington surrounded the British on all sides and forced Lord Cornwallis to surrender at Yorktown. The British were stunned by the defeat. Throughout the war their greatest mistake was continuously to underestimate the Americans. Sadder and wiser, they sailed away and left the Americans to try to govern themselves.

America was grateful to the French for their help in winning the war. General Washington escorted the Marquis de Lafayette on a triumphal tour to Virginia. Patrick Henry was chosen to make the speech of welcome, although he knew not a word of French. The French general understood little English, but when he saw the glowing eyes and heard the rich rolling tones of the orator's voice, he said: "Thees Meester 'On-ree ees great man."

After the war, Patrick Henry was elected governor of Virginia for the fourth time. The most pressing problem he had to solve was: What should be done with the Tories, the many Virginians who remained loyal to England during the war?

"Tar and feather them!" some cried.

No man had spoken more sternly against the Tories than Patrick Henry. The war being won, no man, except perhaps Alexander Hamilton, was more prompt in urging generosity toward the enemy. Governor Henry introduced a bill that allowed them to return in peace to their homes in Virginia.

It took all Patrick Henry's fire and splendor to combat the stubborn hatred of the Tories. "Let us lay aside prejudice," he pleaded in his famous *Lion and Whelps* speech.

"Our greatest want, sir, is the want of men. Those deluded people who sided with the king are enterprising, moneyed people. We need such men to make our nation strong."

He finished his speech with these ringing words:

"As I have no prejudice in making use of the Tories, so I have no fear of any mischief they can do. *Afraid of them!*" He drew himself up, his deep eyes smoldering. "What, sir! Shall *we* who have laid the proud British lion at our feet, now be afraid of his *whelps?*"

So the whelps were permitted to return.

Patrick Henry served two terms as governor — making five in all. Then he retired. "I'm fifty years old," he said. "The governorship has cost me a great deal more than I received. I mean to practice law and make enough money to pay my debts."

The people hated to see him go. Patrick Henry was embroiled in many political squabbles, but his personal popularity never wavered. As far as the people were concerned, he could have been governor for the rest of his life. In Thomas Jefferson's words, "Patrick Henry was the idol of Virginia beyond anyone that ever lived."

chapter 19

The Sun Has Set in All His Glory

DOROTHEA and Patrick Henry sat in their garden enjoying the soft April twilight. Everything seemed to be pearly gray — the sky, the trees, the pond. A whippoorwill whistled in the misty distance. Dorothea understood a man's silence; she waited for Patrick to speak.

"I can't do it, Dolly," he said at last.

"Do what?"

"I cannot go to the Constitutional Convention in Philadelphia. I've made up my mind."

"Why?"

"Because I'm afraid."

"Afraid? That's one word I did not think you knew, Mr. Henry."

"I am afraid of a powerful central government, Dolly." Patrick lifted Dorothea's small hand and held it in his. It helped to talk things over with her. "Young James Monroe wrote me the Northern states want to give Spain our rights to the Mississippi River. I'd part with the confederation before I'd give up the Mississippi. I'm fearful for the South, Dolly. There are six Southern states; there are seven Northern states. They can force through a bill to close the river and we cannot stop it. The North has the power to outvote the South on any issue."

"Then you are against the idea of a federal constitution, Mr. Henry?"

"I believe in the union — you know that, Dolly. But when a great state like Virginia surrenders its rights, we have to be sure we can trust the government that takes them over."

"You said yourself General Washington will undoubtedly be President. Don't you trust him?"

"Beyond any man who ever lived. Men who agree on nothing else, agree on admiration for Washington. But he won't always be here to guarantee the fairness of this constitution. Then what?"

Dorothea's smooth brow wrinkled. "But couldn't you help, if you went to Philadelphia?"

"Help frame a constitution that might end liberty in Virginia? No, my dear Dolly, no, no, no."

Patrick Henry did not go to the Constitutional Convention. Many of the old radical leaders were absent. Thomas Jefferson was our minister in Paris, Sam Adams was in Boston, and Tom Paine was working for revolution in France. George Washington presided at the convention, but James Madison was the one who fashioned the new Constitution.

No one present had ever known a government without a king and it was impossible to please everybody. One main question dominated all discussion: Was the federal government supreme, or were the far stronger state governments supreme? Nation or state, which *should* be stronger? Under Washington's leadership, men who called Virginia or Massachusetts or New York *my* country, began to talk about *our* country.

As soon as the Consitution was finished, Washington sent a copy to Patrick Henry and asked him to support it. Everyone feared opposition from "that overwhelming torrent, Patrick Henry." "I wish the proposed Constitution could have been more perfect," Washington wrote Henry, "but I sincerely believe it is the best that can be obtained at this time."

Patrick Henry put on his reading glasses and studied the document. Then he picked up his quill pen and answered General Washington. "As a citizen I thank you for your great efforts at the late convention. I am sorry that I cannot bring my mind to accord with the proposed Constitution. The concern I feel on this account is really greater than I am able to express."

A convention was called in Virginia to decide if the state would support the Constitution. Eight states had already signed; only one more was needed for adoption. All eyes were on the Richmond convention. It turned out to be a battle of giants. Leading the fight for the Constitution were James Madison, John Marshall, Edmund Pendleton and George Wythe. Fighting against it were James Monroe, Benjamin Harrison, Richard Henry Lee, John Tyler and George Mason — led by Patrick Henry.

Every day except five, during the twenty-three-day fight, Patrick Henry took the floor. "The first thing I have at heart is American liberty," he said. "The second thing is American union. *But* under this Constitution, the Federal government will tax and grow strong. It will soak up power until the states glide gradually out of existence."

More and more the struggle resolved itself into a stunning debate between James Madison and Patrick Henry, one the Father of the Constitution and the other the Father of Virginia. Many of the most learned men of the day sat on the benches listening to them, spellbound. John Marshall said, "If I were asked who, of all the men I know, has the greatest power to convince, I should perhaps say Mr. Madison. But Mr. Henry has, without doubt, the greatest power to persuade."

When Patrick Henry attacked what he thought was the worst defect in the Constitution — the absence of a Bill of Rights — he pulled out all the stops. "I trust, gentlemen, you plan to secure herein freedom of religion, freedom of speech, freedom of the press, trial by jury, and all our sacred rights. If you pass this paper, without a Bill of Rights, you will exhibit the most absurd thing the world ever saw: a government that has abandoned all its powers — the powers of the purse, the sword, and the press — without check, limitation or control."

In the middle of his speech, Patrick Henry caught sight of Caesar signaling him from the back of the room. He knew why Caesar had come. As soon as he could, Patrick excused himself. Caesar shook hands with his master, laughing heartily. "It's *another* boy, Mistah Patrick. Miss Dorothea say this here one's gonna be named for her grandfather Gov'nuh Alexander Spotswood. You shore got yourself a fine passel of sons."

"Thank you, Caesar," said Patrick, grinning with pride. "Great news! No man ever had enough sons."

As debate drew to a close, logic and reason were exhausted. Patrick Henry knew a dramatic appeal to emotion was all that was left him. To him, oratory was the art of making men act differently than they otherwise would. Now was the time to strike. He glanced out the window. A hard wind bent the trees toward the ground. Black storm clouds scudded over the horizon. Patrick Henry, orator, rose to his feet. He was determined to sway the convention. In searing words he spoke of his apprehensions. Throwing his arms above his head, he called upon the powers above to interfere, to reveal the crippling flaws in the Constitution.

There was a terrible crash. Wind shook the building. A furious thunderstorm broke from the sky, rolling and flashing. Rain pounded on the windows, thunder roared. And there stood Patrick Henry, his great voice rolling with the thunder, his eyes flashing with the lightning. His face now hidden, now whitened, as the storm blazed and blackened.

It was unforgettable.

But the storm passed, Patrick Henry subsided, and his stunned listeners regained their reason. George Wythe, still vigorous at sixty-three, jumped to his feet and moved for ratification. In tense silence, the count was taken. Wythe's motion carried by ten votes. Virginia had ratified the Constitution of the United States.

Some of Henry's followers wanted to start a fight against the new government. Patrick Henry refused. He was a good fighter, but a good loser, too. "I did my duty in opposing the Constitution in the proper place and with all the power I have. As true and faithful Republicans, let us go home. Let us give the new government fair aid and support."

Patrick Henry returned to his home, his private life, and the law. He was still in his fifties, but the poison of malaria was in his veins. Bent and haggard, he looked much older than he was. His law practice flourished and

his home life was happy. Four more sons were born to
Dorothea and Patrick, giving them nine children in all.
The last boy, John Henry, was born when Patrick Henry
was sixty years old.

As Patrick grew wealthy, he bought more and more
land. He felt about land as he did about children — the
more the better. Many honors came to him. Patrick Henry
was asked to be:

U. S. Senator, by Governor Henry Lee of Virginia
Secretary of State, by President George Washington
Chief Justice of the Supreme Court, by Washington
Minister to Spain, by Washington
Minister to France, by President John Adams.
All these he refused.

He was elected governor of Virginia for a sixth time,
but again he said no. There was even talk of nominating
him for President or Vice-President of the United States,
but he would not listen. Patrick Henry was through with
public life.

At long last he was able to return to the fields and
woods he loved. He and Dolly settled down at Red Hill,
a large plantation he had bought. Its rich rolling acres
overlooked the Staunton River. There was good hunting
in those parts, but old Langloo was dead and Pat's keen
eyesight was fading.

Always full of fun, Patrick could now spend as much time as he wished playing with his seventeen children and sixty grandchildren. He showed the boys how to build kites and how to make a "slope" across the river to catch fish. He taught the girls to play his fiddle and to

recognize the songs of the birds. One of his grandchildren wrote a poem about him and read it at a family reunion, much to Patrick's delight.

> To The Squire of Clan Henry
> The Belgian hare could nothing to you show —
> Prolific Patrick — how your brood doth grow!
> Not President Washington, but thee
> We should call Father of this Coun-tree.

As age and illness crept on, the habits of boyhood came back. Once more Patrick was careless in his dress and unpredictable in his ways. Visitors often found him playing his fiddle in an armchair under a big oak tree, his favorite drink — a jug of cool spring water — by his side. Here he sat and directed his field hands in the valley below, the great voice carrying easily for half a mile.

One January day in 1799, when Patrick Henry was reading the Bible aloud to his family at breakfast, a letter arrived by special messenger. It was marked CONFIDENTIAL. Patrick recognized the handwriting of George Washington.

Washington wrote to ask Patrick Henry to come to the aid of the government of the United States. Some states, including Virginia, were claiming the right to ignore federal laws they did not like. Patrick Henry did not like some of these laws himself. "But once an act of Congress becomes a law," he said, "it is the *duty* of every citizen to obey it."

It had been many years since Patrick Henry spoke in public. When the word spread that he would speak at old Charlotte County Courthouse, people flocked there to hear him. Nearby Hampden-Sydney College closed for the day. President, professors, and students hurried to the courthouse.

When Patrick Henry arrived, such a crowd surged about him that a clergyman exclaimed in shocked tones, "Mr. Henry is not a god!"

"No," said Patrick, deeply moved by both the scene and the remark, "indeed not, my friend, I am but a poor worm in the dust, as fleeting as the cloud shadows that fly over yonder fields."

When the time came to speak, he arose with difficulty. He stood, bowed with age and weakness, his face lined and pale.

At first his voice cracked, his gestures wavered. But as he talked, he gained power. His bowed head became erect, his blue eyes lit up, and soon his voice rang out like music.

"You have planted thorns in my pillow," he said. "I cannot sleep while Virginia is a rebel to the government of these United States. Even Virginians cannot discard

the laws of Congress. Only the Supreme Court of the
United States has the right to do that. Let us never split
into factions and destroy the union upon which our existence hangs. *United we stand, divided we fall.*"

The vast crowd was silent. Patrick Henry had finished
his last magnificent speech. He was very weak. As he was
carried into a tavern nearby, the clergyman who had rebuked him earlier took off his hat and said, "The sun has
set in all his glory."

A detailed account of Patrick Henry's death was written down by his grandson, Patrick Henry Fontaine. Dr.
George Cabell, the leading doctor in that part of the
state, was with Mr. Henry constantly during April and
May of 1799. Patrick had an intestinal obstruction which
surgery could cure today. But in those days it was different. Dorothea and Caesar hovered over him, but there
was little they could do.

On June 6th, all other remedies having failed, Dr. Cabell handed Patrick Henry a dose of liquid mercury. Taking the vial in his fingers and looking at it a moment, the
dying man said, "I suppose, Doctor, this is your last re-
sort?"

"I am sorry to say, Governor, it is."

"What will be the effect of this medicine?"

"It will give you immediate relief, or . . ." The doctor
could not finish the sentence.

His patient did it for him. "You mean, Doctor, that it will give me relief, or it will be fatal?"

The doctor answered: "You can only live a very short time without it. It may possibly relieve you."

Then Mr. Henry said, "Excuse me, Doctor, for a few minutes." Drawing over his eyes a silken cap which he wore, and still holding the vial in his hand, Patrick Henry prayed aloud in clear words, a simple, childlike prayer for his family, for his country, and for his soul in the presence of death. Then with perfect calmness, he swallowed the medicine.

Dr. Cabell, who loved Patrick, went out on the lawn and threw himself down upon the earth under an oak tree, and wept. When he mastered himself, the doctor went back to his patient. He found Patrick Henry calmly watching the congealing of blood under his fingernails, and speaking words of love and peace to his family, who were gathered around him. "I am thankful to God, who has blessed me all my life," he said, "and who now permits me to die without pain."

Fixing his cloudy blue eyes on Dr. Cabell, with whom he had had many arguments about Christianity, he said, "Observe, my dear Doctor, how great a reality the Christian faith is to a man embracing death. It has not failed me in all my life and it does not fail me now."

He continued to breathe softly for some moments.

Then those who were gathered about him saw that his life had departed, and they wept.

If you visit Red Hill and walk down the garden path, you will come to a square garden plot carpeted with blue periwinkle and enclosed by boxtree hedges. Here, side by side, are two marble tombs. They are inscribed:

Dorothea Dandridge
wife of Patrick Henry
Born 1755
Died
February 14, 1831

To the Memory of
Patrick Henry
Born
May 29, 1736
Died
June 6, 1799
His fame his best epitaph

It was Patrick Henry's old enemy, Thomas Jefferson, who best described Henry's fame. "He was as well suited to the times as any man ever was," wrote Jefferson, "and it is not now easy to say what we should have done without Patrick Henry. He was far above all in maintaining the spirit of the American Revolution."

Bibliography of Principal Sources

Axelrad, Jacob. *Patrick Henry the Voice of Freedom.* Random House, New York, 1947.

Burton, Alma H. *Our American Patriots.* American Book Company, New York, 1898.

Carson, Julia M. H. *Son of Thunder.* Longmans, Green, New York, 1945.

Earle, Alice M. *Child Life in Colonial Days.* Macmillan, New York, 1948. *Home Life in Colonial Days.* Grosset & Dunlap, 1898.

Henry, William W. *Patrick Henry.* 3 vols. Scribner's, New York, 1891.

Hubbard, Elbert. *Eminent Orators.* Putnam, New York, 1907.

Meade, Robert Douthat. *Patrick Henry, Patriot in the Making.* J. B. Lippincott Company, Philadelphia, 1957.

Miller, John C. *Origins of the American Revolution.* Little, Brown, Boston, 1943.

Morgan, George. *The True Patrick Henry.* Houghton Mifflin, Boston, 1887.

Reeder, R. P., Jr. *The Story of the American Revolution.* Duell, Sloan, and Pearce, New York, 1959.

Southworth, G. V. *Builders of Our Country.* Appleton, New York, 1910.

Umbreit, Kenneth. *Founding Fathers.* Harper Brothers, New York, 1941.

Wilstach, Paul. *Patriots Off Their Pedestals.* Bobbs, Merrill, Indianapolis, 1927.

Wirt, William. *Life of Patrick Henry.* M'Elrath & Bangs, 1831.

I also worked with original sources in the New York Public Library and made field trips to Williamsburg, to St. John's Church in Richmond, and to Scotchtown, Patrick Henry's home in Hanover County, Virginia.

Index